OLD McDONALD
HAD A FARM

OLD McDONALD

HAD A FARM

BY

ANGUS McDONALD

ILLUSTRATED BY

RICHARD BARTLETT

HOUGHTON MIFFLIN COMPANY · BOSTON

The Riverside Press Cambridge

1942

The Riverside Press
CAMBRIDGE . MASSACHUSETTS
PRINTED IN THE U.S.A.

NOTE

This book is about my father, James Angus Mc-
Donald, and how he labored to make a good farm
out of a poor one. I lived on this farm with him
and my brother, sister, and mother from 1912 to
1922, near Sallisaw, Oklahoma.

CONTENTS

THAT IS THE WORK OF THE DEVIL

THE old man and I stood at the top of the two long slopes that ran together and formed a draw. In the draw was a long deep gully.

'Look at that gully,' he said. 'See how it is eating up this land.'

From where we stood we could see where it started and where it ended. At the beginning it was a little thing almost concealed by the half-dying vegetation, while farther down the hill it was very big and very deep.

In Oklahoma, in the summertime, we nearly always had a drouth, and this year the dry spell had been unusually long so that the corn was burned up and even the cotton was beginning to suffer.

There were small gullies which ran into the big one. If you looked closely, you could see the tiny tributaries reach out like fingers that were trying to cover both sides of the slope.

'Son,' the old man said, 'look closely. You are seeing the thing that is undermining our country. This was once good land, and look at it now. This gully has ruined a good hill farm.'

The hill farm was a mile from Sallisaw, the little town where the old man and my mother and my brother and sister and I lived. Sallisaw lay in a little valley in the foothills of the Ozarks in eastern Oklahoma. To the south of the valley lay a low long-flung chain of hills called Wild Horse Mountain. Each succeeding hill to the north was larger than the other. The fourth one, which we had just walked over, was about a mile from the town. The sides of this hill were especially steep facing the town, and the road was rough with great rocks. To the north were more hills, but they were smaller and less abrupt, while the valleys in between were large enough for big farms. Farther north, however, the hills began again, but this time they were much larger. Finally they disappeared into low-lying chains of small mountains. Brushy Mountain, which formed the north horizon, disappeared to the east and west.

Back of these mountains was the famous outlaw country where men like Henry Starr would go and hide after they had robbed a bank. That section was known as the Cookson Hills and was where the natives made whiskey

and protected outlaws. Not a man, woman, or child
would reveal the hiding-place of a fugitive. Sometimes a
killer would hide in the hills, but it often was not considered necessary in the early days of Oklahoma. Many
of the inhabitants had a code of justice which had no need
of courts. Usually, when a man killed another no one
bothered him because the community considered the
killing was an execution and not a murder. Often the man
was not even arrested.

The old man said that the wickedness of Oklahoma was
what caused him to go there to preach. He said that
Oklahoma was bound for hell as straight and as fast as an
Indian could shoot an arrow.

The old man, at this time, was sixty-one years old, and
although he was at the height of his physical and mental
powers, I always thought of him as old. He was like the
hills, the sky, or the soil that he loved so much. We all
thought of him as something apart from the usual run of
fathers or men. He had a certain austereness about him
that made us fear him, although, when he was in a good
humor, we laughed and talked and even wrestled with
him without restraint. I think my mother must have had
the same feeling about him too. She never called him by
any other name except Mr. McDonald. In speaking of
him to us, she referred to him as your Papa. We called
him Papa occasionally, although in our hearts, or at least
in mine, he was the old man.

He was to me the man who stood head and shoulders
above all other men and he was the old man who was old
yet ageless; old yet virile, vigorous and strong. I find it
hard to believe that he ever was young.

He was born in 1850 in a log cabin in Alabama, the son of Alfred McDonald, who claimed descent from William Henry, a first cousin of Patrick Henry, the Revolutionary hero. His ancestors had fought in every war since 1750 when they came over from Scotland. The McDonalds were farmers and Presbyterian preachers — Calvinistic, stern, intolerant, but poor.

When the Civil War came, the old man was ten years old, and after his father went to war he, being the oldest, supported the family. The years of starvation weakened his mother so that at the end of the war she sickened and died. Then it was up to him to take care of the five children that had been left behind.

But at the age of eighteen, when he was out plowing one day, he received the call. The Lord spoke to him and told him to go preach the Gospel of Jesus Christ. When he told his father what had happened and how the Lord kept repeating the command, his father released him from his family duties and the old man went out in search of learning.

Although he was soon ordained and preached every Sunday, he was resolved to get an education. He went to Cooper's Institute in Mississippi, working, preaching, farming — doing everything he could to earn the money to see him through school. From there he went to Lebanon, Tennessee, where he got a degree. In the meantime he had married and had two children. He finally graduated at the age of twenty-nine with the highest honors. His wife graduated with him in the same class.

From then on he served the Lord, living in towns and cities preaching the Gospel and saving souls. But he always wanted to get back to the farm. He read about better methods of farming and he looked at farm land and talked about getting back to it as if he had just left it. That was how he happened to be looking at the gullied fields of the hill farm that day.

The old man continued to stand and look at the big gully. 'You can't see it now,' he said, 'because the farmer has plowed over the rills, but last spring during the wet season the water washed out the young cotton plants and carried away the richest soil. Notice how yellow the soil is in these little depressions. And look farther down where the little gullies start.'

The plow of the farmer had dragged some loose dirt into the gully, but in many places the bottom of it was slick and bare. On its edges was a little crab grass scorched by the July sun. The whole hillside looked sick. The stunted cotton stalks were wilting and even the cockle-burs were turning yellow.

Scattered over the hillside were a few piles of rocks thrown up hastily to get some of the biggest out of the way so that the field might be plowed. The little rocks, particularly near the top of the hill, cluttered up the rows so that you couldn't move without stepping on one.

The farmer had once tried to work the land where the second growth now was, but the rocks were too much for him, and now there were larger spots of hickory and oak sprouts that grew almost as high as your head.

'Now look at the right-hand side of the slope,' said the old man. 'What a fool the farmer is to try to raise corn on this hill land.'

The corn field looked even sicker than the cotton field.

The blades of the stalks were yellow; the bottom blades completely dead, and the top ones, while still a pale green, were twisted into all kinds of shapes. Some of the corn was still in silk and tassel, and I could see the little ears beginning to form on the sides of the stalks. Had it not been for the drouth, the pollen would have fertilized the slips by catching onto the little silks. It was obvious that the tassels and the pollen were dead, and many of the silks looked dead too.

Both fields had an air of dry sickness about them. All the vegetation was burning and the hot south wind seemed to wilt the growing things all the time. The grass, the weeds, everything but the dog fennel with its yellow blossoms forming a fringe around the dying fields, looked sick.

In between the two fields was the giant gully which sucked the life out of the vegetation. Or at least so I imagined as we gazed at the desolation.

'Look at the little gullies,' said the old man.

At their beginning the depth was almost imperceptible. The tributaries emerged on the one side from the field of cotton and on the other from the field of dying stalks of corn. But a little way down the slope there was no mistaking them. They grew deeper and wider.

The giant gully also was small at the top, and some of the rows of cotton ran across it, but a little way down, where the two slopes came together, it formed the dividing line between the two fields. It became so deep that it would have been impossible to drag a plow across it.

And what a giant it grew into halfway down the slope. At its beginning its sides were slanting, but farther down they became perpendicular and we could see great chunks of overhanging soil ready to fall into it. It was at least ten feet deep.

I was tired of standing and looking at the burning fields. So I was relieved when the old man said, 'Come, let's go.' But I was disappointed when he headed for the gully instead of turning to go back home.

'I want to look at the lower end,' he said. We walked down the long slopes along its banks. Every little while the old man would stop and climb down into the gully and shake his head and measure its depth with a long stick he was carrying. Then he would climb back on the bank and look up and down the hill before going on. We walked in this manner for a half a mile, stopping at intervals down the long slope.

'This gully,' the old man said when he had climbed down, 'is at least fifteen feet deep. It would be a tremendous job to fill it.'

Toward the bottom of the slope it began to flatten out. Its sides were less abrupt and finally it disappeared in the flats below.

'Well, sonny,' said the old man finally, turning to me, 'let's get back.'

Going back to the house where the farmer lived, we traveled a different way. We circled around and came up on the east side of the farm through more stunted cotton fields and more fields of twisted yellow corn. There were gullies on the other side, but none of them equaled the big one on the west slope.

The whole top of the hill seemed to be a mass of rocks. In order to make a road to the barn, the farmer had thrown some of the biggest ones in piles.

The main characteristic of the little farm we had walked over was disorder. The fields of corn and cotton, like the piles of rocks, were scattered at random over the hill. Here and there were blackberry bushes, weeds, patches of dog fennel, clumps of second-growth timber of hickory, oak, and sassafras. The fences were down in some places and a single strand of barbed wire was stretched across the gap to keep the stock out.

As we approached the barn, its dilapidated rundown condition was the first thing we noticed. The roof was sagging in the middle and the support of one of its corners was rotted clear away. It looked as though it might fall at any minute. The stalls were full of manure and it was evident that they had never been cleaned out. Even the work animals looked like the other things about the farm. In the lot stood a broken-down team. The two old bags of bones were standing disconsolately in the hot sun switching the flies off each other. There was an old red cow standing in the dog-fennel patch that grew in the lot, her hips sticking out sharply and her bag shrunken. Probably she would give only half a gallon of milk a day. In an adjoining pasture was an emaciated calf which bawled piteously.

The house looked even worse than the barn. It was made of logs and had only two rooms. The window-panes were out and the old rock chimney was falling down; the roof was made out of homemade boards and had holes in it over which were tacked pieces of tin. There were old quilts and rags tacked around the two small windows, but these had been partially removed to let in the air and were flapping in the wind.

In front of the house two dirty children played list-lessly. As we approached, a man and woman came out of the cabin talking. We had walked quite close before they saw us.

'What do you want?' the man asked. 'What are you doing on my place?'

'I want to know who owns this land,' said the old man, ignoring the man's rudeness.

'Old Doc Kelleam rented this land to us,' replied the man.

'I noticed you didn't have any garden or chickens. A good farmer always has a good garden, a few pigs and chickens. You renters would get along better if you raised more stuff to eat.'

'What do you want?'

'The foundation of a good farm is livestock and feed crops. The manure will enrich the land and you can eat the pigs and chickens, and raise a garden that will keep your table supplied with fresh vegetables.'

People around Sallisaw were used to the old man's lecturing them about how to farm. And although he was laughed at behind his back, the people took his preaching on soil conservation good-naturedly.

But this man was different.

'Look here, mister, I don't know what you want, but why do you come and tell me how to run my farm?'

'I am a preacher. It is my duty to give advice where it is needed.'

'Well, preacher, you stick to your preaching and I'll stick to my farming.'

The old man was beginning to get angry. 'Well, some

of you farmers could stand a lot of preaching about the land. All of this here' — and he waved his arm toward the gullied fields — 'that is the work of the Devil. It is a work against God. God's work should be carried on seven days a week, not just on Sunday. God never intended that farmers should butcher up land. You and other farmers have ruined a good hill farm.'

'You tend to your own business,' responded the man, and turned and went into the house.

'Ignorant churn-headed fool,' muttered the old man, half to himself and half to me, as he started back to the road where he had left the horse and buggy.

The old man stood and looked at the barren rocky little farm before he unhitched the horse from a post-oak tree. Then he turned and looked down into the valley where the little town lay. 'Yes,' he said again to himself, 'it is close enough for the boys to walk to school.' Then he turned and looked at the north horizon. 'Plenty of open range for the dry cattle and mast for the hogs the year around. Plenty of timber near-by. Yes, the location is good.'

Going home, the old man talked of how he had been wanting to get back to the farm for forty years. We were crowded into the buggy seat together with his legs spraddled out so that I was pushed into a corner.

We drove down the dusty road that led to the little town of Sallisaw, the old man clucking and slapping at the horse. He had no horse and buggy of his own; he had borrowed this one from his brother Henry.

When we entered the little town with the railroad running along its northern border, we turned and proceeded down the front street. First we passed Uncle Clayton's store that had hanging over it a big sign, CLAYTON McDONALD, GENERAL MERCHANDISE; and then at the end of the block was a still larger store that Uncle Henry owned. Across the street on the other corner was the First National Bank, where Uncle Henry had an office.

When we got to this corner, we turned and traveled a few blocks south down to where Uncle Henry lived. The old man had to return the horse and buggy. After he had unhitched and fed and put the horse in the barn, we walked to where we lived, which was only a few blocks away.

'Well, sonny,' the old man said, 'how would you like to live on a farm?' And without waiting for me to answer, he went on talking. When we approached our house, he noticed a wagon and team in the yard off to one side. The mules were tied to a tree and their trace chains were dropped.

'Well, I declare!' he exclaimed. 'That looks like Green's mules and wagon. I'll sure be glad to see Green.'

Uncle Green was the old man's youngest brother and in some ways his favorite kinsman. He had been a delicate, sickly child, and the old man, who was always hale and hearty, looked after Green, who was just a little fellow when his mother died back in Mississippi.

The old man's father used to look at Green when he was a boy, and shake his head, and say, 'I declare I don't know what's the matter with him; he must be wormy.'

As we went in, we met Uncle Green. He was a thin, round-shouldered man of medium height, slightly stooped and flat-chested. He had a rather bushy mustache, a high forehead, and a look of solidness and stability about him that characterized all the McDonald brothers.

'Hello, Jim,' he said. 'I had to come to town to get some flour and thought I'd stop by and see you on the way out.'

'Glad you did, glad you did,' the old man responded. He was always delighted to see any of his brothers. 'How's your health been lately?'

'Oh, I've been rather poorly of late,' replied Uncle Green. 'How have you and your family been?'

'Fine, fine,' said the old man. 'These boys are growing fast; they'll soon be big enough to work.'

'That's right. You know, Jim, you ought to have these boys on a farm.'

'Don't I know it! Don't I know it! And that's what I'm going to do. I'm going to get a home place close to Sallisaw.'

'It would be nice if you could locate out at Price's Chapel,' said Uncle Green.

Price's Chapel was a country schoolhouse about five miles from Sallisaw. Uncle Green lived on a farm near-by with his wife, my Aunt Jennie, and their large family of boys and girls.

'No, Green, I want to get a farm near Sallisaw close enough for the boys to walk to school. Their education must not be neglected. Of course, Beatrice will have to go to school too.'

That night at supper the old man told of his experiences of the afternoon. 'What an ignorant fool that farmer is,' he said. 'Why can't Doctor Kelleam get a better renter? It is a burning shame the way people in this country abuse the land. A lot of them are like this ignorant fellow. It's no use to talk to them. If I go out to look at the place again, I'll not have any more arguments with the renter. It's no use.'

'Why are you going out to look at the place again?' asked my mother. 'You say it is no good, rundown and rocky.'

'Never mind, wife, never mind. I didn't say the place wasn't any good. I didn't say it couldn't be built up. But of course it would take a lot of work.'

'Papa,' asked my sister, 'wouldn't it be better to buy a place that's already built up?'

'Well, of course, that's what your mother thinks. She's lived in town all her life and doesn't understand that a man can improve a farm cheaper than he can buy another man's improvements.'

'I have no objections to your buying one,' said my mother. 'That's all you've talked about ever since I've known you. You'll never be happy until you live on a farm.'

'Yes, that's right,' said the old man. 'I'm sick of the city. I've been living in cities for forty years, and what have I got to show for it? And furthermore, when I move on this place, I'm not going to raise any cotton. It has been the ruin of the South and nobody should raise it.'

'Farmers in Sequoyah County have got to raise cotton,' said Uncle Green. 'How could they get any money if they didn't?'

'Green, that's where you're wrong. Ever since I've been living in Sallisaw I've been telling these farmers that if they'd raise stuff to eat instead of cotton, they'd get along better.'

The old man had moved to Sallisaw in 1906. The following year the Indian Territory was made a part of the State of Oklahoma. The old man had been pastor at the First Presbyterian Church in Fort Smith for several years, but he had seen a great opportunity to build up the church at Sallisaw, so he accepted a pastorate there. He liked it better because it was a smaller town, because Oklahoma was a new state, and because his brothers, Henry and Clayton, lived there.

He persuaded Uncle Green to sell his farm at Mountainburg, Arkansas, and come out to Price's Chapel.

My mother had little to say during this conversation between the brothers. She knew that it was futile to give the old man advice. He never paid any attention to the family's suggestions, though he was always asking for them. He demanded the approval even of us children. If we disagreed in the slightest or expressed an opinion contrary to his, he promptly said we were fools and became very angry.

All his talk about what a wonderful place the farm was, and how American farmers were abusing the land, we agreed with enthusiastically. We could hardly do otherwise. The old man demanded it. He insisted that his ideas not only be agreed with, but that his discipline and the rules of the household and the family be strictly adhered to. For example, he did not believe that there should be any hilarity or cutting-up during the meal. We came to the table to eat. That was serious business. First the food must be blessed. We must thank the Lord for each mouthful, and how could we be in a proper spirit if we were clowning and giggling?

Consequently, there was always a tendency for us to be

amused by everything that was the least bit funny. The slightest joke would throw us into gales of laughter, and I remembered many's the time when my brother and sister and I almost choked trying to keep a straight face during the meal.

The worst incident that I remember occurred that night when Uncle Green was visiting us.

It is customary, of course, to have the visitor return thanks, so the old man asked Uncle Green to bless the food. We had never heard our uncle do this and we did not realize the treat that was in store. He yelled at the top of his voice, 'O dear Lord, bless this food and consecrate it to our needs...' but with each word he kept lowering his voice until in a few seconds the words were completely unintelligible, and anyway he said them so fast you couldn't have understood them even if they had been audible.

This threw my sister and brother and me into the most side-splitting fit of laughter you can imagine. Even my mother giggled a little. We tried to stop, but it was impossible. Any attempt to swallow our food resulted in loud shrieks.

The old man pretended not to notice at first; soon he reprimanded us, but it did no good. We were in such a state of hysterics that we couldn't control ourselves.

'Daughter,' the old man finally said, 'you may leave the table.' And my sister ran away. We heard her hysterical laughter in the next room. A moment later, my brother and I followed. We all rolled on the floor and laughed to our hearts' content. My mother, too, caught the mood of hilarity and burst out again. In a minute she joined us. Between gales of laughter she said, 'Your Papa sent me away from the table too.'

We came back in a few minutes after we had straightened our faces. Uncle Green pretended not to notice the merriment.

My mother was a sweet soul and had adapted herself to the discipline of the old man, so when he began preaching the virtues of a farm life, she agreed, and I remember in my earliest childhood that she pointed out many of its advantages to us.

The old man, however, always insisted that she opposed his going to the farm to live and that she, being a city woman, could not understand or appreciate rural life.

So that night at supper, when he asked Uncle Green's advice about buying the hill place we had looked at that afternoon, he said to us children, rather contemptuously of my mother as if she were not there, 'Of course, your mother probably won't like the idea of leaving the city.'

And my mother, who had long since found out that no matter what she said the old man would hold to his original notion, was silent.

2

YOUR MOTHER IS A CITY WOMAN

MY MOTHER was not a country woman, having lived in small towns and cities most of her life. But she grew to desire a permanent home, which seemed possible only on a farm. She had had a hard time ever since she married the old man. When she first met him, he was a widower with five children; and the pastor of the Presbyterian Church in Union City, Tennessee, where she was a school-teacher. My mother was always religiously inclined, having been active in church work ever since she was a young girl. It was natural that she should become acquainted with the pastor, who was the best-dressed, best-looking, and most brilliant man in the town.

Miss Emma, as my mother was called, had seriously considered going to China, to be a missionary to the heathen. Now along came Brother McDonald, and she soon saw a great opportunity to do a lot of good as mother to his children and at the same time to follow her heart's desire.

Before the old man proposed, he went to Effie, his oldest daughter, and asked her what she thought of his marrying Miss Emma. Effie, having been a second mother to the children, had acquired a maturity far beyond her years. Usually children frown at the idea of anyone's taking the dead mother's place.

'Papa,' she said, 'if you love Miss Emma and want to marry her, I think you should do so. I will do all I can to smooth the rough places.'

And she was true to her word. There never was the slightest misunderstanding between her and my mother. 'We never had a cross word,' said my mother.

Effie took the lead and disciplined the other children to meet the new situation.

My mother devoted her life to them. She gave herself whole-heartedly to their interest and in a short time had made them love her almost as much as they had their own mother.

The youngest, Katherine, was only four when the old man and my mother were married. The others, Mary, Dessie, and Foster, were older than Katherine and younger than Effie.

My mother's marriage was opposed by her family, who

did not believe she should sacrifice her life to a widower
and five children. She had been a frail girl, having been
sick most of her life. Her mother, whom I remember as a
granite-faced old woman who never complimented us children except behind our backs, tried to stop the match.
'I would just as soon see you dead,' she had said to my
mother. 'You'll be in your coffin if you marry that man
with all those children.'

But my mother's mind was made up and, although she
was a soft, sweet soul who never provoked a quarrel or
rarely said a cross word, when she set her head there
was no stopping her. On most things she was apt to give
in for the sake of peace and harmony, but occasionally
she would fortify herself behind her principles and her
Scotch-Irish determination, and from there you couldn't
budge her.

In her relations with the old man she was that way.
She gave in to him on almost everything. But once in a
long while she would set her head, and even he, who was
as stubborn and hardheaded a person as I have ever
known, would back down.

Those times when she came into opposition with the
old man or anybody else were few and far between. For
the most part, she was the peacemaker of the family.
She was constantly adjusting difficulties between the old
man and the stepchildren, and later between him and me
and my brother and sister. The fire and nervousness of
the old man often came into conflict with the fiery tem-
peraments his children had inherited or acquired from him
by association. My mother's rôle was to hide her personality. She was constantly accommodating her thought,

speech, and action to the children, who, like the old man, were prone to dominate others.

On the morning before my mother's marriage in Union City, an old friend of hers who lisped remarked prophetically, 'Poor Misth Themma, poor Misth Themma, the's eaten her lasth peathful meal.'

This statement proved to be almost literally true, for no sooner had my mother got the older children started on their careers than she began to have babies of her own.

Five children in all came. Two died, which left my sister Beatrice, who was four years older than I, and my brother Worden, who was four years younger. Worden, the last of the old man's ten children, was born in Sallisaw, where we were living at the time he decided to buy a farm.

The old man's nervousness and irritability due to insomnia caused us children some unhappiness. He had acquired the habit of not sleeping in his college days. Many a time he would toss and tumble all night long, only dropping off to sleep about daylight. Then we would have to tiptoe around the house without making the slightest noise. It was on those occasions when we would forget and laugh and play that we would feel his anger. He would come roaring out of the bed, saying that he couldn't sleep in this bedlam.

Then we would talk in whispers until he finally went to sleep, or, despairing of any, would get up.

He always held it against my mother that she was such a good sleeper. 'Your mother doesn't care,' he would grumble sometimes, 'if I die for lack of sleep. There she lies night after night dead to the world while I am going crazy with sleeplessness.'

Sometimes he would thrash around in the bed and throw his arms wildly and hit my mother, causing great bruises and black-and-blue spots to appear on her body. But she never complained.

'Your poor Papa,' she would say, 'he is almost crazy for lack of sleep.'

At the time the old man picked out the Kelleam farm to buy, his insomnia seemed to be getting worse. That was one reason he wanted a farm. He felt, as we all did, that on a farm, where he would be out in the open, he would be able to sleep.

That was a strong inducement for us to make the change. My brother and sister and I knew that we could have more pleasure on a farm, if for no other reason than that the old man would be less hard to get along with. We hoped that there he wouldn't interfere with our playing so much.

There were other reasons too. We were very poor and we thought that on the farm we would be rich. We would have horses to ride and plenty to eat and many new ways to enjoy ourselves. The old man painted a glowing picture of farm life. He said that we would never go to town without coming home with a pocketful of money. 'I will give you boys all the money you can make selling chickens, pigs, and vegetables,' he said.

He also said we would be kept out of mischief. We wouldn't be loafing around pool and dance halls and other bad places. We were hypnotized by all this talk, and came to feel that if we didn't get out of town we were bound straight for hell.

Cities, the old man believed, were responsible for wickedness. 'Jefferson was right,' he would say repeatedly. 'The morals of a country depend on a free and farming population.'

These and other similar ideas we got from the old man, and we used to try to explain them in our way to the neighbor children. The boys around Sallisaw had a far different idea of farm life.

Cousin Hub, Uncle Clayton's boy, who lived next door to us, told us the farm was a bad place to live because we would have to work all the time. 'Oh, my poor back, you'll be saying,' he said to us one time. 'My poor back hurts so from leaning over these cotton rows. Besides,' he added, 'everybody knows that farmers are rubes and hicks.'

But the argument of our city cousins did not change our belief.

There was one topic of conversation, though, that all the boys of the community always agreed on, and that was what fine people bank robbers were. There was a great deal of admiration for them because they were so brave and generous and because it was said that they took from the rich and gave to the poor.

Henry Starr was the most famous bank robber of our generation and one of the best-loved men in the community. No doubt many of the stories about his exploits were untrue or exaggerated, but they were all believed by the young boys. He was looked up to more by the young boys in Sequoyah County than any other individual.

One of these stories was that Henry Starr was not really to blame for his life of crime. He was unjustly accused of stealing a horse or had had some other crime pinned on him. He had to become a fugitive and naturally he was forced to rob banks after that.

Then there were stories about Henry's shooting ability. It was said that he could shoot a chicken's head from the hip with his pistol. It was said that he never aimed. He shot by instinct and he never missed. In spite of Henry's great shooting skill, however, he never killed a man. That is, unless it was forced on him.

The old man didn't like Henry Starr. He said that he was a grand rascal and that he ought to be locked up for good.

When I was a little fellow I went with the old man, who visited one of Henry Starr's relatives, I believe an aunt, at Porum.

This old Indian woman did not agree with the Robin Hood stories that were going around about her nephew. 'A no-good, that's all he ever was, Brother Mac,' she said, and she took her pipe out of her mouth and spat contemptuously into the open fire. 'He never was no-good. He wouldn't work and he robbed because he was so mean. I won't allow the no-good to come on my place.'

But most of the people in and around Sallisaw did not agree with Henry's aunt. They respected and admired him. And my brother and I agreed with all the stories about the nobility, the gentleness, the bravery, and the shooting skill of the great man.

So it was a great thrill to me when I finally saw him. I had come to town with the old man and he had gone into the bank to talk to Uncle Henry when I ran into Jess Scott.

Jess was a schoolmate of mine and was the 'fightenist' kid I ever saw. He could lick boys twice his size. He wasn't a bully, though. He never picked a fight, but it was just too bad if somebody picked on Jess.

'Hello, Mac,' he called to me. Although we were both children, he always called me 'Mac' in the fashion of grown-ups. 'Henry Starr is in town,' said Jess. 'Henry Starr is here!'

'Henry Starr!' I exclaimed. Now that I was close to the local hero, I felt panic-stricken.

'Well, don't you want to see him? I'll show him to you. I know him well,' said Jess, throwing out his chest.

'Sure,' I said, 'sure I want to see him. Sure I do.'

'Well, all right, follow me.' And Jess led the way across the main street and over to the Iron Mountain depot. There were a number of people gathered around on the platform waiting for the train to come in.

'Now look down at the other end of the platform,' said Jess.

'I don't see anybody.'

'Don't you see that little man standing there?'

'Sure, I see some man down there, but that's not Henry Starr. That couldn't be.'

'Sure it is,' said Jess. 'Let's walk by careless-like. Now, don't look at him too close. They say he doesn't like to be stared at.'

We walked by Henry Starr where he was standing evidently waiting for a train.

I was greatly disappointed. He didn't seem to be any different from any other part-Indian. He was of average height and build, even a little on the small side.

He didn't pay any attention to us, but he began talking in a low voice to someone who came up to him. When the train came in, he left. Evidently the person he was looking for didn't come in.

We followed him — at a distance, of course — and he walked over to his horse which was hitched back of Uncle Henry's store and rode away.

'Well, what do you know about that!' I exclaimed. 'He's just as mild-mannered as you please. I don't believe he was even carrying his guns.'

'What did you expect him to do?' asked Jess. 'Come into town shooting? He's probably making his plans to rob your uncle's bank. That's the way with old Henry,' Jess said admiringly. 'Old Henry's never the one to blow and brag and make a fuss. No, sir, he just goes about his business quietly. That's the way with genuwine bank robbers. They don't put on airs.'

Perhaps one reason why we admired bank robbers so much was because we were so poor.

I remember the last Christmas before we went to the farm and how the poverty of the family made the distant pastures look so green. At this time the old man's salary was very low. There was scarcely money for the necessities, much less for luxuries. And the old man considered Christmas presents definitely luxuries. He never gave anybody anything for Christmas that I can remember. He was always glad to get presents himself, although he pretended not to be.

He had gone to General Assembly as usual. He would not miss one of those church congresses no matter how hard up he was. He was always promising to take my mother with him on one of his trips. But there never seemed to be enough money.

This year there was not a penny to spend on anything extra. Usually each child received a certain amount of money to buy presents for the other members of the family, but this year there was no money at all. On Christmas Eve we had to eat corn-meal mush and milk for supper.

So it was with woe-begone faces that we hung our stockings up. We really didn't expect anything. We had learned at an early age that there was no Santa Claus, because my mother did not believe in lying even about folk tales.

We felt pretty blue that night when we gathered to eat our mush and milk. Even the old man, who ordinarily was not affected one way or the other by holidays, seemed a little downhearted. Holidays he considered a lot of foolishness, except that they gave more time for prayer and study of the Bible.

My mother, as usual, tried to add a cheering thought. 'Just wait, children,' she said brightly, 'wait until we get on our farm. We'll have fried chicken every day.'

'Eat your supper, Beatrice,' said the old man. 'What's the matter with you, child?'

My sister was sitting at the table, but after the food was blessed had made no move to eat. This Christmas was hardest on her because she realized better than Worden and I what poor prospects there were.

'I don't want any supper, Papa,' said Beatrice, and burst into tears. Then she ran from the room.

Ordinarily the old man would have made her come back and finish her meal, but tonight he said nothing. He seemed to understand what was wrong.

Worden, who was too little to understand what it was all about, caught the spirit of the despondency, however, and began to blubber. He yelled just on general principles, I guess.

I sat and sulked, blaming my parents because there was no money for Christmas.

'Well, children, hurry and get through with your mush and milk,' said my mother. 'We have to go down to the church, you know, where they are having a tree. Who knows, you may get a present there.'

At that we perked up a little. At the Presbyterian Church in Sallisaw it was the custom to have a tree and a Santa Claus on Christmas Eve every year, with bags of candy for the boys and girls. Sometimes there were cheap presents too.

Sunday-School attendance always jumped away up just before Christmas. All the rowdy boys who cut up in church and Sunday School became very good. They did this so that Santa Claus would remember them at home and at the church too. My mother taught a class of the big boys because she was the only one who could handle them. They got almost out of hand sometimes, even with her.

The old man had formerly been the pastor of the First Presbyterian Church at Sallisaw. But a few years after he had accepted this church, he saw, as he said, a chance to do more good and he accepted a traveling job. It seems that the Board needed somebody to travel around Oklahoma and establish new churches. The old man was just the one for the job. He was a good mixer and a good organizer, and he could raise money for a new church building where others failed.

So for the past few years he had been organizing new churches. It was a tough job because Oklahoma was a new country full of such works of the Devil as moonshine whiskey, gambling, and other meanness. But the old man liked a good fight and he went into the back country and carried on the work of the Lord with a great deal of energy and success. 'I have built in Oklahoma,' he said, 'more churches, spiritually and physically, than any other man.' He had built a church at Sallisaw and a big manse with an immense hall where we could have socials and family reunions.

The old man was a great one for family reunions. He thought that the McDonald clan, as he called them, was the best stock. 'Stock is what counts,' he said. 'Good blood will tell in the end. Good strong honest Scotch blood, that's the best in the world.'

He looked forward to the time when he would have a big house where all the older children and their families could come and visit and eat all they wanted. On the farm that would be possible. But not, of course, under our present circumstances.

When the old man gave up the church at Sallisaw he had to give up the manse, and we lived in a little tacky green-painted house whose chief characteristic was that it had three front doors, all of them identical. The rooms were small and the paper was falling off the walls, and on cold nights the wind whistled through the cracks. This was no place to entertain. Rather, we dodged company. We were all ashamed of the house.

That night something went wrong at the church. Old Mitch Steffens, who was supposed to play the part of

Santa Claus, got drunk and there was no one else available. My mother took his place.

Old Mitch was one of the town's drunkards. The old man had brought him into the church at Sallisaw when he was pastor and he had got him to stop drinking, but after the old man left he began again. The new preacher couldn't do much with him. He always got drunk on holidays. He still claimed to be a good Christian, though, and regularly repented after every drunk.

But he couldn't resist temptation and the Devil got him by causing a great thirst to come on him. So that night he was stone-blind drunk when he should have been worshiping the Lord and celebrating Christ's birthday by giving out presents to children like my sister, brother, and me.

My mother took his place and, though her voice sounded a little strange behind the Santa Claus whiskers, she did a good job. We each got a bag of candy and a little present of something or other, I've forgotten what.

This little celebration cheered us momentarily, but we went to bed with heavy hearts, for our thoughts had returned to the bleak prospects of Christmas presents at home.

The next morning we did not get up early as is usual on Christmas because we had little to look forward to. Our mother came in and woke us, telling us to go see what Santa Claus had brought.

We filed into the front room where we had hung our stockings, and to our surprise found a lot of presents inside and stacked in piles beside them. There were horns, drums, and other toys, and books and clothes.

Naturally we were very happy, particularly since it was such a surprise. My mother had been saving out a few pennies for Christmas all that year. In her characteristic way she had made up her mind to give us a nice Christmas and had allowed nothing to interfere with her plans, even though it meant mush and milk for supper on many a night.

3

YOU LEND MONEY ON COTTON FARMS

OLD Doctor Kelleam, who owned the hill farm that the old man wanted to buy, was one of the town's leading physicians. He had come to Indian Territory in the early days and had married into a leading family of the Cherokee Nation. When the Indian land was allotted, his children and his wife each received eighty acres.

The Doc, as everybody called him, was given poor land. Many of the Indian allotments were more or less worthless. The hill place was a part of his wife's property.

One morning the old man called on Doc Kelleam and he took me with him.

'Hello, Doctor McDonald,' he greeted the old man. 'Hello, sonny. Have a chair. Since you've got that traveling job we don't see you around much. We sure miss you in the church here.'

'You never went to church. How do you know?' replied the old man.

'Oh, you know I'm so busy with my practice I don't have much time to go to church. Besides, the Devil has got me in his clutches and won't let go.' And the old Doc laughed loudly and pulled his beard, which was a habit of his when he was deviling somebody. 'You preachers just keep trying, though. You may save me yet.'

'If you weren't such a rascal, you'd be the best man in the community,' replied the old man. 'I'll say one thing for you, you do a lot more good carrying on the Lord's work doctoring poor people for nothing than a lot of these city doctors who sit on the front row and lead in prayer on Sunday and sock big bills to people who can't afford to pay. These city doctors don't know in a day as much as you know in a minute. I always did say that the old-fashioned home remedies would cure ailments better than a lot of these new-fangled methods. I know there's nothing better for a cold than bathing your feet in hot salt water and tying an old greasy sock around your neck. Many's the winter night when I went to bed with a sock around my neck soaked thoroughly in goose grease. The stronger the sock the better. If it has been worn a few weeks and thoroughly permeated with toe gum, it works on the cold faster' — and the old man laughed loudly.

'Well, you may be half right at that,' replied Doctor Kelleam. 'A lot of these home remedies are O.K. Some of the old Indian herbs are the best things in the world for some types of diseases. A few of them have been handed down for centuries in certain Indian tribes.'

'In my family,' continued the old man, not listening to the Doc, but thinking of what he was going to say all the time the other was talking, 'turpentine and coal oil have been used for a long time. In my opinion it was the only thing that saved Henry's life. You know Henry had a bone felon on his finger and I remember that he kept it in turpentine and coal oil all one night. His finger has always been stiff since, though.'

'Yes, I remember Henry's finger. You McDonalds are all so stubborn, you won't go to the doctor. It's a wonder Henry lived through that. Blood poison set in and I wanted to cut his arm off. But he was so stubborn, he wouldn't call me in the first place, and wouldn't take my advice, in the second. You damn McDonalds,' said the Doc, stroking his beard, 'are the stubbornest damn family in the country.'

The old man was a little annoyed at the 'damns' which the Doc always used when he wanted to tease religious people, but he was not unpleased at the reference to the McDonald stubbornness. He was proud of it. He liked to think that once he made up his mind, he never changed it.

'What I wanted to talk to you about, Doc,' he said, abruptly changing the subject, 'was a piece of worthless land you own out north of town. I was wondering if you had made any money on it lately?'

The old man knew full well that the hill place wasn't paying.

'Made any money! I haven't made any money on that

hill since I owned it. It is the sorriest no-good land in
the country. The Government sure played hell with my
wife's rights. They gave her the highest, driest, rockiest,
most unproductive piece of land in the country.'

The old man smiled. When the doctor saw this, he
exclaimed, 'But what are you bringing this up for?'

'I thought you might want to sell a part of the hill farm.'

'Yes, I might sell if I get a good price,' he said, changing
his tone. 'You know we were thinking about making a
homestead out of that farm. It would make a nice
country home.'

The old man laughed. 'You just told me it was the
sorriest land in the country.'

'Oh, well, yes, in some ways, but it would be a fine
location for a home and a chicken or fruit farm.'

'Well, Doc, I just thought you might want to sell,
but I see I was mistaken. I didn't know you were going
to make it your home place.'

'Now wait a minute,' said the Doc, when he saw the
old man was getting ready to go. 'Why don't you make
me an offer?'

'I don't like to price another man's stuff,' replied the
old man coldly, and he started for the door of the Doc's
office.

'I'll tell you what, Brother Mac. You go out and look
at the farm and I'll talk business. I know you can see its
possibilities.'

'All right,' replied the old man, 'but I don't know that
I'm interested. I'm afraid you'd want too much for it.'

That day the old man went around to Uncle Henry's
bank and talked to him in the back office.

'Henry,' he said, 'I've got my eye on a piece of land, the Kelleam place out north of town.'

'Yes, I know the land, Jim. But why are you interested in the Kelleam place? It is nothing but a pile of rocks. I don't think there is an acre of good land in the whole farm.'

'Yes, I know, I know,' replied the old man impatiently, 'but then it has more possibilities than appear on the surface.'

'Well, I don't know what money you could make off that pile of rocks.'

'Money, money, that's all you think of. Because you're getting rich, you think there's nothing in this world but money.'

Uncle Henry laughed. He was a little man, but he had a quiet sureness about him that made people respect him. He always paused before he answered a question and frequently, when his opinion was asked on something, he wouldn't reply. He'd just look up, tilt back his head a little, and look at the ceiling or the sky. He was superintendent of the Presbyterian Sunday School and in church the preacher always called on him to lead in prayer. No wonder! He probably contributed most of the preacher's salary. When he prayed, he never closed his eyes like the other elders. He just looked up and you felt he was looking right at the Lord.

So when the old man chided him about loving money too much, he laughed at first, then his face grew solemn and he looked up like he did when he was talking to the Lord in church.

'I have never made a dishonest dollar, Jim. In the store, I've always given full measure.'

'Oh, Henry, I didn't mean you weren't honest,' said the old man.

'I remember,' continued Uncle Henry, 'when I started to work for the Reynolds' grocery store at three dollars a week in Fort Smith, I asked Mr. Reynolds what the rules were and he said, "Give a pound for a pound, a full sixteen ounces. Never misrepresent any merchandise. Be honest in every way. Treat the customers right." Well, Jim, I followed this rule, and when I went into business for myself, I always told my boys and my clerks the same thing.'

The old man became impatient. 'Never mind, Henry. I know you are honest in your business, but you must remember there are other things besides money. A good life is more important, and you can only have that on the farm.'

Uncle Henry shook his head. 'You like the farm, Jim. All right, you move out there, but I'll stay in town if you please and make money, as the good Lord intended me to. How could I support the church if I didn't?'

'Well, Henry, how about coming out and going over the Kelleam place with me today?'

'All right, Jim. I guess I can get away for a couple of hours.'

Uncle Henry and the old man and I drove out that afternoon. This time the old man talked a great deal about what he would do with the farm if he owned it. 'I will make a nice home place out of this rock pile.'

Uncle Henry shook his head. 'Jim, this is the biggest fool thing I ever heard of. Why, this land is no-good. And anyway, if it was, you couldn't farm it on account of the rocks.'

'Henry, that's where you're wrong. There's a use for even those rocks. The Lord has a use for everything he made. That is, except for dog fennel and cockleburs, I guess. You see these gullies. How do you think I could get them stopped if it weren't for these rocks? I'll build big rock dams across them, and in a few years they'll be filled in. You know, every time it rains, a little soil comes down the sides of these hills. Well, if I can slow down the water it will drop the soil in the gullies and eventually fill them up.'

'Jim,' replied Uncle Henry, 'you'll never be able to work it. Why, there's not enough soil on the hill to do that.'

'You wait and see.'

'Anyway, if you did fill them up, you'd still have a poor farm. It would cost more to build up the place than the land is worth.'

The old man didn't continue the argument. I could see he was a little vexed with Uncle Henry for not seeing things his way. He set his mouth in a firm line and changed the subject. 'Henry, one reason I wanted you to look over the place was that I wanted to borrow some more money at the bank. The land won't cost much, but I want to build a nice roomy two-story house with a sleeping porch.'

'Jim, I don't believe the bank would be willing to lend you money on this land. We are already carrying your notes on the Greenwood Junction place and that's all you're able to pay.'

The old man had borrowed money from Uncle Henry to buy the Greenwood Junction farm and he could only make payments if he rented the land to cotton farmers.

He had a great deal of respect for Uncle Henry's business judgment. Uncle Henry was getting rich. Already he owned, besides the store and stock in the bank, the cottonseed-oil mill and a thousand acres of bottom land.

Not that the old man always took his advice. In fact, Uncle Henry had advised him against buying the Greenwood Junction farm. Finally, Uncle Henry let him have the money and sure enough the wet land became good land except in a flood year. In Oklahoma we often had rainy seasons that caused the bottom land to overflow.

'Yes, but you forget that I would be living here and would save my rent and get my living from this farm,' the old man said.

Uncle Henry laughed. 'Mark my words, Jim. You'll never be able to make a living off these washy hillsides. It would cost you more to keep up this place than your rent.'

'Most of the money I wanted was for the house,' the old man went on, ignoring Uncle Henry's objection. 'I guess I'd need about twelve hundred dollars for that and four hundred dollars for the land.'

'Now, Jim, I don't think you'd be able to get Delaney to approve a loan like that. Of course, if you were buying good cotton land, it would be different.'

During the weeks that followed, the old man made many trips to the bank and talked several times with Mr. Delaney, who was Uncle Henry's partner. He would go in and talk and talk and both Mr. Delaney and Uncle Henry would shake their heads. He also called on Doctor Kelleam several times.

Finally one day the old man stomped out of the back

office. I had been waiting on the outside and I heard him say, 'All right, all right, if that's the way you feel. But it's bankers like you who have caused this country to go to rack and ruin. You'll lend money on cotton farms. Cotton, cotton, that's responsible for the ruin of the South. But you don't want to lend money on a farm that's going to bring in a living.'

Uncle Henry and Mr. Delaney both followed the old man out into the front of the bank.

'One reason, Brother Mac,' Mr. Delaney said, 'that we're a little doubtful about this loan is that you wouldn't even be here to tend to the farm. Your pastor evangelist job keeps you away most of the time. We doubt if you could make a living, much less any money on something that you'd leave to the direction of someone else. Besides, you haven't lived on a farm for forty years and farming has changed a lot.'

'So my pastor evangelist job is what's worrying you. Well, I'll tell you what I'll do. Here's my proposition. If I can get a pastorate near the farm, will you approve the loan?'

'That would make it a better risk, Jim,' said Uncle Henry, 'but how do you know you could get a church in this county? There's no opening here.'

'I'll get some churches near the farm,' he told Uncle Henry. 'I've already been looking around a little.'

Soon after that the old man resigned his traveling job and took on the job of organizing churches back in the hills.

He got the Board to assign him three new country churches — Price's Chapel, Badger Lee, and Dwight Mission. He planned to preach at Dwight twice a month and at the other two places once a month. Badger Lee was only about two miles from the Kelleam farm and Dwight Mission was about ten or twelve miles away. Price's Chapel was four miles north and east of the hill place.

'Well, Henry,' he said one day when he had dropped in at the bank again, 'I've made all arrangements for pastorates near the farm so there shouldn't be any objection to my getting the money.'

'I still think it's a bad risk,' commented Uncle Henry. 'You'll never be able to make a living out of that pile of rocks.'

'Wait and see,' was all the old man said. He was tired of arguing, I guess.

'Have you spoken to Doc Kelleam about buying the land?'

'Yes, I've mentioned it to him several times. He's all ready to close the deal. And why shouldn't he be? That farm has never made him a dollar.'

After this was settled, we made frequent trips out to the farm and the old man was busy with plans. He had lumber hauled out, and he hired two hands to start cleaning up the place.

He had some difficulty with the renter, though. The man had possession until the first of the year and wouldn't move, although he had gathered his crop. The old man caught him stealing timber one day on the back side of the west field.

The old man and I walked over the farm and looked at the giant gully for the hundredth time.

On the upper side of the field was a little patch of white oaks. Some of those trees were almost two feet thick.

As we approached the little grove, we saw the man and woman that we had seen the first time we had walked over the place, pulling a cross-cut saw.

'What are you doing cutting down my timber?' the old man shouted.

'I'll cut a tree for firewood if I want to,' replied the man sullenly.

'You'll not cut any on my place without my permission. Get your firewood from the dead timber. There's plenty lying around.'

'What difference does cutting a few trees make?' asked the man. 'When I rented this place, the Doc told me that I could take all I wanted.'

'Yes, and I told you the other day that I bought this place and that I didn't want any timber cut. Why, that's as fine a tree as ever I saw. I ought to make you pay for it.'

'Now, listen, preacher, I've taken enough from you. I've got this place until the first of the year and you haven't got no business telling me what to do.'

'Why, you timber thief,' yelled the old man, 'I'll throw you and your rags out into the road if you fool with me.'

The man muttered something and picked up a rock.

The old man became angrier than ever when he saw this. He walked over closer to the man and yelled, 'Drop that rock, you rascal!'

The man was so surprised, he dropped it. The old man walked up close and looked him in the eye. 'If I catch you stealing any more of my timber I'll thrash you and prosecute you besides. It's trifling no-account farmers like you that have ruined this country. You cut all the timber off these hills and planted them to cotton. You've butchered a fine country. Well, you're not going to butcher this land any more.'

Then he walked back to the road. 'I'll be glad when that scoundrel vacates the place,' he said to me. 'I may lose my temper with him yet.'

Many times I've seen him in such a rage that he'd slam the door so hard every window in the house would rattle. 'Wooden cussing,' my mother called it. But he never once admitted that he'd lost his temper.

The framework of the new house was started in December, and although the weather was bad, the old man drove out every day. He used Uncle Henry's horse and buggy.

All the old man's friends and relatives (and he asked advice of everybody) told him to build a one-story house. 'A two-story house is liable to blow down,' they said.

But the old man insisted on a big eight-room two-story house with a big attic and two porches. 'I want a big house so I can look down at you city folk,' he would say. 'That's the reason I bought a high hill farm. I want plenty of fresh air. I want my place to look up into the sky, not squat down like a hog.'

When the frame of the house was up, a storm came and blew it down. We went out to the farm the next morning after the big wind. There were broken pieces of boards and timber scattered all the way down the hillside. The old man looked a little blue when he saw the wreckage. 'Mr. Alfred,' he said, turning to the contractor, 'I want you to build this house so strong no wind will ever blow it down. Put on three layers of lumber, one on the inside, one for the outside, and on top of that a good stout layer of weather-boarding.'

'All right, Brother Mac, but it's going to cost considerably more.'

'Never mind the cost,' said the old man.

I couldn't believe it when I heard him say that, because he had always counted every nickel. Some of the neighbors said he was so tight he'd skin a flea for its hide and tallow. Every time my mother asked him for money, and of course she had to once in a while to buy clothes and food, he would say, 'I haven't any money,' and then he would add — because we knew he always kept some money on hand in the bank — 'in my pocket.'

But he certainly didn't spare the expense in building up the hill place. Already it was beginning to change. There were rolls of barbed wire, hog wire, and fence posts stacked up. Some of the hands had started piling up the biggest rocks near the house and tearing down the old rickety outhouses.

The hands also worked at cutting sprouts. The old man was out there every day early and didn't leave until dark. The house was gradually going up and occasionally one of the neighbor farmers would stop out of curiosity.

One day the old man and I were piling rocks when a man came along and introduced himself. 'My name's Irwin,' he said. 'I live on the place below yours. Heard you had bought this place.'

'I am always glad to meet a good farmer,' replied the old man, shaking hands. 'W. H. said you were one of the few good farmers in the country.'

'Well, I manage to make a living on twenty acres without raising cotton,' said Mr. Irwin.

'What!' exclaimed the old man. 'You don't raise cotton! You must be a good farmer. I never did see a cotton farmer who didn't ruin his land.'

'You're right, Mr. Mac. Come, I want to show you my little place if you've got the time.'

'I've always got the time to look at a good farm.'

Mr. Irwin's twenty acres lay under the hill just south of our place. It was as neat and pretty a little farm as you ever saw. Looked like a garden. Everything laid off in little patches. He had many varieties of fruit trees and his garden must have covered an acre. Of course, it was winter and nothing was growing except rye and turnips, but you could see that he kept his place in good shape. All the fences were up. There were no loose wires and the rows of his crops led clear up to the fence. 'I use every foot of land I've got,' he said.

'It does me good to see your farm. I am going to make a good farm out of the Kelleam place too.'

'Well, I don't want to discourage you,' said Mr. Irwin, 'but you'll find it a hard job. It's not like my place. Of course, none of this land was ever very rich to begin with, but at least it wasn't so rocky and it is fairly flat. Your hill place is different. The top of the hill seems to be a mass of rocks and the sides are pretty bad too, with big deep gullies down them.'

'I intend to stop the gullies and pile up those rocks,' said the old man.

'You'll never get those big ones stopped, I'm afraid. Of course, it won't do any harm to try except that it'll be an awful expense.'

'Well, anyway,' said the old man, 'you've got a nice farm. You are doing a good job here. I have one suggestion, though. Whether you know it or not, you're losing quite a bit of soil on the north side of your place where it runs up against the hill a little way.'

'How do you mean losing soil?'

'I mean every rain washes a little of it away. Look!' And the old man walked across the field. 'Do you see that little gully there and some little rills leading into it?'

'Well, now, Brother Mac, I don't think that amounts to much. But, anyway, how could I stop it?'

'Run your rows on the contour instead of up and down the hill. That will stop some of the wash. Of course, putting the land in some close-growing crop would be good.'

'You may be right about that. I generally run my rows across the hill, but this year one of the hands laid them off and I didn't notice until afterward that they were run down the hill. I was behind in my work and let it go.'

That night at the supper table the old man told the rest of the family about Mr. Irwin and his farming. 'At least there's one good farmer in the country. But you just wait and see. I'll make a good farm out of the hill place. Soon we will be moving out and then you boys can go to work. I am glad to be getting you boys away from the city.'

Sallisaw at that time was a town of about fifteen hundred.

'It's no place for a boy. What does a boy do in the city? He loafs around the pool halls and gets into trouble. The criminal element comes from the city. Thomas Jefferson was right when he said that cities were evil.'

'When are you going to take over your new pastorate?' asked my mother.

'I start in about two weeks and it's going to be a tough

job. Badger Lee is a wicked community. Of course,
Dwight Mission won't be so hard because the church has
had an Indian school there for about a hundred years. I
think it was in 1816 that Dwight Mission was established.
Next Sunday I have been invited to preach here at
Sallisaw.'

'Isn't Aunt Lu coming in from California?' asked my
sister.

'Yes, Lu will be here, and your Uncle Henry was telling
me Alice and Doc are coming in from Fort Smith next
Saturday. We'll have a big family reunion. Green and
Jennie will come in from Price's Chapel.'

The following Sunday the McDonalds gathered in the
church house at Sallisaw that the old man had built when
he had been pastor. They and their families half-filled the
church. They had all got along well, 'prospered,' as the
old man said, 'in the nurture and admonition of the Lord,'
and were blessed by large families. 'The McDonalds,'
he said, 'are a prolific bunch.'

Before the services, Cousin Tabby went up to the old
man. 'Uncle Jim,' she said, 'when you preach today,
please don't talk about the family.'

She said this because the old man liked to brag about
what hard-working poor people the McDonalds were. He
thought it was a great honor to be the son of a poor Mississippi farmer who had made his first crop with a blind
mule and spavined steer.

Poor Cousin Tabby had had sad experiences with the
old man when he had been pastor at Fort Smith. He had
humiliated her by telling personal things about the family.

One reason he liked to talk about his poor ancestors

and what a hard time they had was because some of the present generation were making a lot of money and putting on, as he said, 'a lot of blue-bellied airs.'

'Never mind, Tabby, I never tell anything I'm ashamed of,' the old man said. 'I'll never be ashamed of my old daddy. He was poor and he lived in two rooms and ate out of tin plates, but, except during the war, he always had meat in his smokehouse and he never owed a man a dollar he didn't pay.'

The old man took as his text the story about the three talents, and while he made it clear that the Lord wanted people to make money, he wanted them to make it honestly. Work was his theme. He said that hell was primarily for the lazy people. To be lazy was the biggest sin he could imagine.

'Farm life is responsible for the industriousness of the people of this country. My generation, the people that are running this country, all learned to work on a farm.

'And let me tell you one thing. I am going back to the farm where I can teach my boys how to work. And some of you who have been putting on a lot of airs should go and do likewise.

'There was a time when our people were not ashamed of work. I remember after the war everybody worked on our farm near Tupelo, Mississippi. The girls chopped cotton and we boys plowed it. Yes, Alice and Lu worked in the fields and I venture to say they are not ashamed of it today.

'I remember Alice could pick more cotton than any girl in the neighborhood. She was a little trick, but she was quick. She always could pick more cotton than Lu.'

I was sitting between Aunt Alice and Aunt Lu, and I noticed Aunt Alice looked pleased, but Aunt Lu frowned and bit her lip. As soon as the service was over, she flounced down to the pulpit where the old man was. She was as mad as a wet hen. 'It's not true, it's not true, Jim. How could you tell such a thing?' exclaimed Aunt Lu.

'What?' asked the old man.

'I could pick just as much cotton as Alice.'

'Oh, Uncle Jim, you've ruined us,' Cousin Tabby said. 'I can never hold up my head again. How can you tell such awful things about the family?'

'Never mind, Lu,' said the old man, ignoring Cousin Tabby. 'I'll tell the people next Sunday you were a good cotton picker too.'

'Oh, Uncle Jim,' said Cousin Tabby, 'you'll ruin us. I will never be able to hold up my head in Fort Smith society again.'

4

YOU WON'T KNOW THIS PLACE IN A
YEAR

IN THE spring of 1912 we moved to the farm. I was nine years old, my brother was five, and my sister was thirteen. We were too little to do much work, but we were assured by the old man that it would not be long before we would be making full hands in the field.

However, we could pick up rocks and put them in piles, pull weeds, and help the old man in other ways. There were a lot of fences to build and we children were very useful. We ran errands and handed the old man and the hands tools when they needed them.

One of our hands was a little fellow named Charley, but he was sprightly as could be and a very hard worker. He talked incessantly when anybody would listen. He used to make jokes about the old man to us children. He claimed that the reason the old man had to wear glasses was that he had worn the corners of his eyes out watching his hired hands.

The old man did watch the hands pretty closely, because he didn't like them to loaf on the job. He didn't like too much conversation either, if it interfered with the work. But Charley worked right along whether he was talking or not, so the old man couldn't object.

Charley was sensitive about his strength and his ability to hold out. 'I may not be very big,' he said, 'but I never did see the man that could work me down.'

The other hands that the old man depended on that first year were Dave Daggles and his boys. The Daggles family lived just a short distance down the hill from us. The old man had bought the top of the hill, so to speak, and the land on the north side. Our land extended just a little way down the hill, and south of our yard fence was Dave Daggles' cabin. He lived in one room and had about eight or ten children. The oldest was named Dee, a big strapping fellow who never did much work.

The Daggleses had the reputation of being trifling people, but the old man got along with them well. 'I never met a more clever fellow than Dave Daggles,' he said.

Dave was poor as could be, but the most accommodating fellow you ever saw. He worked sometimes by the day and the old man paid him the customary dollar and dinner, but lots of times he would help the old man out when he was in a tight place and wouldn't charge a penny.

The old man liked people to work cheap. And even more he liked presents. It was the custom of the country for everybody to give the preacher something, and often when he went visiting he'd come home with fruit and vegetables.

It takes a lot of work to build up a rundown place. There is plenty to be done on a farm that is in good shape to begin with. But this place was a real eyesore. There were piles of old rubbish lying around, and here and there twisted pieces of barbed wire, old buildings, and outhouses falling down, weeds and thickets and blackberry patches. But the old man kept repeating that he was going to change all this.

'You won't know this place in a year,' he told the neighbors, and they just shook their heads and smiled.

First of all, he cleaned up the front part of the farm. He cut out all the thickets, trimmed the larger trees, and ran a fence around the house including about an acre and a half of ground.

'I like a big yard,' he said, 'with lots of shade trees.'

Back of this he made two lots — one for the cows and one for the horses; and back of the lots he fenced off two more acres. 'That will be the garden,' he said. North of the house he fenced off two more acres. 'That will be the orchard.'

The neighbors laughed when he talked about his orchard. A horse could scarcely walk through that land for the rocks, big sand rocks of all sizes scattered over the ground. Some of them were so large that one man could scarcely turn them over with a crowbar. 'They'll come in handy when I get to building dams,' the old man said.

That spring we moved to the farm — we didn't build many dams. There was too much else to do. The old man was more interested in getting the land ready for a crop. 'After the crop is laid by,' he said, 'we will build dams.'

Soon after we were settled, he bought a team of young mares. Just before he closed the deal, he noticed a buggy sitting in the barn lot of the man who owned the team.

'Nice little buggy,' he said, and he went over and walked all around it, lifted up the shafts, and shook the wheels to see if they fitted snug on the axles. Finally he climbed up on the seat.

I didn't see anything so fine about the buggy. In the first place, it was a cut-under type. The bed didn't run from the front to the back. There was an open space under the seat so that the front wheels wouldn't lock on the bed. It was made this way so that you could turn short, I suppose, but it spoiled the looks of it and left little room to carry anything in it.

But for some reason the old man was particularly attracted to this type of buggy. I suppose because it was so old-fashioned. All of the modern styles had wide beds running from front to back so that a lot of stuff could be carried in them. Another bad thing about it was that there was no protection against the rain. But the old man didn't seem to mind this either. He walked around it again and repeated, 'Nice little buggy.'

Mr. Mabray seemed a little annoyed when the old man left the mares and went over to the buggy and began talking to himself.

'Well, let's get on with the deal, Brother Mac,' he said.

'I tell you what I'll do. I'll take your price. I wouldn't
do this for anybody else. But you being a preacher, I'll
let you have the team for two hundred and twenty-five
dollars.'

Mr. Mabray and the old man had been haggling for
a month over that team. The original price had been
three hundred dollars, and I thought he would jump at
the terms of two hundred and twenty-five dollars. It had
taken the old man three weeks to get Mr. Mabray down
to two hundred and fifty dollars. But strangely enough,
he didn't seem to hear him. He just kept looking at the
buggy and walking around it.

Mr. Mabray was annoyed. He had spent a lot of his
time bargaining with the old man and naturally he wanted
to close the deal.

'Well, Brother Mac,' he said, 'do you want the team
or not?'

'I'll tell you what I'll do, Brother Mabray' — and I
could tell by his tone of voice that he was going to get
some further concession out of him. He always called the
person 'Brother' when he wanted something. 'I'll tell
you what I'll do,' he repeated. 'We'll close the deal on
this team of mares if you'll throw in this old ramshackle
buggy.'

'Ramshackle buggy!' snorted Mr. Mabray. 'That's as
sturdy a little buggy as you'll find anywhere. Why, I just
had it painted and had brand-new shafts put on it.'

'But the style of the buggy is out of date,' said the old
man. 'Besides, it has no top and the dashboard is bent
and there's a hole in the upholstery. One of the wheels
is out of line, it looks to me.'

'Well, all right, Brother Mac,' grumbled Mr. Mabray,
'I'll throw in the buggy. You are the hardest man to trade
with in the country. I'll declare you are. Take the team,
take the buggy, and take the harness that you wanted
thrown in too, and give me a check and I'll give you a
bill of sale.'

Mr. Mabray was a big jovial horse-trader and cattle-
buyer who never got out of humor, but I could see that
he was a little vexed now.

'All right, Brother Mabray,' said the old man. 'I'll
bring a horse down and get the buggy tomorrow.'

We hooked the team up to the new John Deere wagon
that the old man had bought. The young mares seemed
very excitable and unbroken, although Mr. Mabray had
told the old man that they were gentle as lambs. 'They'll
make a fine work team,' he had said.

The old man didn't seem to mind their skittishness. 'I
like a horse with spirit,' he said. 'Now this young mare,'
he continued, pulling back her lips and looking at her
teeth, 'is a fine animal. She's only three past; hasn't got a
full mouth yet. And she's a fine saddle animal. I rode her
out in the country with Mabray the other day. As pretty
a fox-trotter as ever you saw.'

The other mare, who was a year older, had a white star
in the middle of her forehead and seemed a lot gentler.
She didn't prance around so much and champ her bits.

'Mr. McDonald, don't you think you had better put
J.I.C. bits on this team?' said Charley, who had come to
town with us. 'They seem awful hard-mouthed.'

'Never did see a horse I couldn't hold with a smooth
bit,' replied the old man.

'That team'll run away at the drop of your hat,' remarked a stranger who had been standing watching us hook up the team.

The old man looked around at the man sharply.

He was a tall, thin, stringy fellow who must have been about fifty or sixty years old. You could tell by his high cheekbones and his beardless face and his black hair and eyes that he was an Indian.

'How do you know?' asked the old man.

But the Indian did not answer. He merely took out his snuff can and stick and began packing snuff in his lower lip.

When the team was all hooked up and ready, the Indian put one foot on the front hub. ''Lowed I might ride a ways with you,' he said. 'Live near Badger, other side of your place. Know Mabray. Saw this team run away once. Name's Choate, Josh Choate.'

'Climb in, Choate, glad to have you,' replied the old man. 'You know I'm building a church at Badger.'

The man did not reply. He merely stepped up on the brake block, then up onto the step and into the wagon. Then he squatted down in the back, saying nothing.

The team lunged forward. The old man, who was sitting in the front with Charley, braced his feet and checked them a little. The team didn't walk or trot; they danced all the time and lunged at intervals. They proceeded this way down the main street of Sallisaw.

Sallisaw was one of those little one-street towns with the railroad on one side and the town itself on the other. As luck would have it, there was a train coming. Now, if there's one thing an excitable, untrained horse is afraid of,

it's trains. So when the train rounded the long bend above
the town and pushed its giant black nose at the trembling
young mares, they bolted.

The old man braced his feet and from where I was
standing I could see the lines cut into his hands. But in
spite of his great strength (and I have never seen a man
who was stronger), he couldn't hold that team.

The train was coming toward us, so naturally the horses
veered off to one side. The old man pulled on the right
line to keep them in the street and they began running
sideways. They ran clear off the street and across the
sidewalk up onto a Bermuda grass lawn.

It was a through train and did not stop at the town,
so it was gone in a minute. Then the old man got the
team straightened out and back in the road and we went
home.

'Mr. Mac, you oughtn't to keep that team,' said
Charley, when we got them back on the road. 'They'll
never work. That's mustang stock. It'll never be harness-
broke.'

'A fine team,' chuckled the old man, 'a fine team.
Good spirit. See how they hold their heads. There's good
blood in them. See how Nell holds her head.'

The mare Nell certainly did hold her head high, almost
straight up in the air. Her tail, which was long and thin
and strong, stuck out so straight you could see lather
running down between her legs. All around the breeching
and the backband and the collar you could see the sweat.
And no wonder. She had been running for half a mile and
still was dancing up and down like one possessed. Her long
tongue bobbed in and out of her mouth and you could hear

her loud breathing, while slobbers ran out of her mouth.

The other mare, Star, was dancing around some, but she was calming down. Anyone could see that Nell was the more fiery one.

We finally reached our farm and I got out to open the gate that the old man had built.

Already you could see change. There was a big high hog-wire fence clear around the big yard and the weeds and sprouts were gone.

Scattered over the yard were hickory and oak trees with the lower branches neatly removed, and the front of the yard was sodded to Bermuda grass. The old man had had the sod hauled out from town.

'I want to get a lot of Bermuda started early so next year we can start some grass pastures.'

The old man stopped and the Indian crawled out of the wagon. 'Mark my words,' he said, 'this wild team will kill you and your family.' And without another word, he turned and walked off down the road.

'Strange fellow,' muttered the old man, looking after him. 'Probably a full-blood. Acts like one.'

That spring the team improved some, though Nell was still so skittish that she was liable to run away any time. If you dropped the lines for a minute, she would break into a dead run.

A lot of the jobs on the farm involved using the horses. The old man worked them every day. There was manure to haul, plowing to be done, and trips to be made to town.

'Brother Mac,' said Uncle Dave Daggles, 'I tell you one reason your team is so wild. You feed them too good. Now the way to keep a wild mustang animal toned down is to cut down on his feed. You take my horse Heavy. Now there ain't a finer animal in the whole country.'

'You mean that old bag of bones? Why, that horse is no good,' said the old man.

'Brother Mac, you don't know Heavy. She is one of the best work animals in the country. But I can't feed her much. If I did, she'd be a lot meaner even than your stock.'

'Well, Dave, you run your stock and I'll run mine,' said the old man.

That first year everything seemed to go wrong. In the first place, we had got a late start. There was so much work to be done that the old man couldn't get his corn planted early enough.

In Oklahoma, a drouth comes almost every year in June, which lasts, every once in a long while, clear into August. If you get your crop planted early enough to get the benefit of the spring rains, the corn will almost always be made by the time the drouth comes.

Of course, the old man wasn't planning to raise much corn on that hill — that is, not until he got the land built up; but he said there were three acres over on the north side that would raise corn. He hauled manure from the old stable and spread it on the garden spot back of the house, and what little was left he spread on the three acres.

'It's too late to manure that land,' said Charley. 'It won't rot quick enough for the crop to benefit.'

'I know it, Charley,' said the old man, 'but I can't help it. It should have been turned under last fall.'

When we were hauling manure we had one of our

numerous runaways. I was holding the team while Charley and the old man were loading the wagon.

'Go to the house and get us some water,' said the old man to me. 'Let your brother hold the horses.'

Worden was a little fellow and I was afraid he couldn't hold the team. If Nell found out he had the lines, the chances were she would run away.

'But ——' I started to say.

'What's that?' asked the old man sharply.

I said nothing and handed the lines to my brother and started to the house after the water. Maybe Nell won't know the difference, I thought. She has the blind bridle on and can't see unless she looks around.

Halfway to the house I heard an awful yell. Sure enough, the team had run away and jerked my brother down. Fortunately the wagon didn't pass over him. The team didn't go far, just across the lot, because the fence stopped them. But the wagon tongue and breast yoke were rammed into the fence. If there hadn't been three strands of barbed wire the team would probably have run right through it. After that the old man watched them more closely.

In the late spring the slow rains came and warmed and fertilized the seeds that we had planted. You could see the little stalks of corn thrusting themselves up through the soil. And in the garden the beans and the peas and the other plants popped out of the ground. They grew larger day by day and their color changed to a deep, rich, dark green. The sunshine and rains warmed the old hill and made it come to life.

The trees, too, came to life, and the branches and the

little green twigs sent forth showers of leaves which soon hid the brown bare limbs. The oaks, the hickories, the persimmons, the sassafras bushes, all burst out with green, and the sprouts we had cut sent out shoots which turned into leaves.

The farm changed from brown to green. The greenness extended even into places where the rocks almost covered the ground. From between the rocks sprigs of grass and heads of weeds appeared. Dog fennel, cockleburs, ragweed, crab grass, lamb's-quarter, and iron weeds appeared everywhere, crab grass most of all, and covered the ground with a fine green rash.

The rains and warm weather brought all these things to our farm. And scarcely had we noticed the green things we had planted growing according to the old man's plan than we saw this flood of vegetation that had come to plague us.

Weeds and crab grass are the farmer's greatest enemies in Oklahoma. They choke out the crops so that they cannot grow. They suck all the nourishment out of the ground so that the defenseless plants sicken and die.

But the old man was ready for them. Already he was sharpening the hoes, buying small cultivating plows, and making other plans to get rid of the enemy.

5

I AM RUINED! WORLD WITHOUT END!

FIRST the old man took small plows and cultivated the young plants. It was a hard job, because they were easily covered up and killed by the dirt thrown by the plow. The old man used a double-shovel stock equipped with two slender calf-tongue plows, and he began training the young mares to walk slowly by the side of the rows. First he would run the plow on one side of the row of little corn plants, stopping every few feet to uncover one with his foot. The purpose of this was not only to stir the ground, but to cover up the little growth of grass that was appearing in some places as thick as hair on a dog's back. Then he would run the plow down the other side, lapping the moist, freshly plowed earth in the row, and throwing up earth around each stalk of corn. About eight days later he plowed the corn again with a Gee-Whiz, and after that we thinned it and cut out all the weeds between the rows.

We had to hurry to keep ahead of the grass, for it grew very fast, speeded up by the warm rains which came every few days.

The garden required most work of all, for there were many plants which had to be tended with a hoe — a much slower job than plowing.

We also had to get all the tomato and cabbage plants started that were now big enough to set out. The old man took the little plants and set them out with a great deal of care. Then we children watered them until they started growing well, then cultivated them every few days. The old man had a big sweet potato patch too. He had bought a bushel or more of fine seed potatoes and had made a bed out of manure and rich dirt. He watered the beds with warm soapsuds. He said this was to make the potato plants grow faster.

When the plants were big enough, he pulled them up and set them out very carefully. The ground had been thoroughly prepared. He broke it twice after having manured it and then harrowed it three or four times so that it was well pulverized. Of course there was not nearly enough manure in spite of the fact that it had been accumulating in the old ramshackle barn for years.

'You wait,' said the old man to nobody in particular. 'I'll have enough one of these days. Every farm should be a manure factory. You wait and see.'

After the ground was prepared, the old man threw up ridges with a turning plow and dragged them down again, and then took a sharpened hoe handle and made holes about eighteen inches apart along the tops of the ridges.

Behind the old man walked my sister, dropping the sweet potato plants one to each hole, and behind her, I came. I pressed the roots down into the hole, almost filling it with moist dirt. Then we took a sprinkler and watered. All of this work was done in the late evening so that the sun wouldn't wilt the newly set-out plants. The next morning we were up bright and early and watered them again, and finally filled the hole with dry dirt.

The old man was very happy on these occasions when he put the whole family to work. He insisted that even my mother help out, though there was plenty for her to do in the house, what with cooking for the hands, churning, mending, washing, and the thousand and one tasks that a woman has to do on the farm. For a city woman, my mother certainly worked hard.

I remember what a pride the old man took in his family on those occasions when we were all busy in the big two-acre garden.

'I tell you, wife,' he would say, 'we'll make a go of this yet. We'll be mighty hard to starve out in a few years. All of these vegetables' — and he looked at the neat row of young plants of tomatoes, cabbages, sweet potatoes, and all the others — 'will keep the table supplied with more food than we can eat.'

At other times he got excited at the inroads of the grass and weeds and said they'd swallow up the whole farm.

That year I got my first thrill of handling a plow and

watching the moist fresh dirt roll over. The old man let
me plow with Star and a double-shovel. He wouldn't
trust me with Nell, who, though she was far more intelli-
gent than Star, was still apt to run away if you didn't
watch her.

Nell was a little tricky too. I could never catch her
in the lot. One time she kicked me when I was trying to
corner her. She had just been shod and you could see the
marks of her shoe on my leg. It formed a semicircle of
blue.

I didn't let the old man know what had happened,
though. He had promised to let me plow that day and I
was afraid of his displeasure if he found out. He would be
angry at Nell, and at me for getting in the way, and would
more than likely put me to pulling cockleburs or piling
rocks, jobs I had already come to dislike.

So, although my leg hurt all day, I didn't tell anyone.
My mother came out in the afternoon and I sat down on
the side of the row and drank some lemonade and ate
some sandwiches that she brought out. She knew that a
growing boy gets tired and hungry and thirsty in the long
hot afternoons and she had brought some refreshments.
This was a habit she early acquired on the farm. She was
always bringing us out ice water, lemonade, or some other
refreshments when we were working.

This was my first day as a real 'hand' and I was very
proud. The old man was busy on the other side of the
field and had come over to inspect my work several times.

'Well, son,' he said, 'you'll make a farmer yet. You are
handling that mare all right and you are lapping the dirt
in the drill.'

I was plowing corn with a double-shovel and it took some skill. The horse had been trained to walk in the right place, but you had to guide her at the end so she wouldn't step on any corn, and you had to drag the plow around to the other side of the furrow or to the next row so there wouldn't be any corn plowed up. Then the plow handles had to be held up in just a certain way so the shovels would not go too deep or too shallow or get too close or too far away from the little stalks of corn. But I enjoyed the work and the moist loamy dirt felt good on my bare feet. Still, I was glad enough to sit down and rest a little when my mother came out.

'Don't you think you have plowed enough for today, son?' my mother asked.

'Oh no,' I said. 'I like it. If I stopped I would have to pile rock or pull cockleburs.'

After a little rest I continued throughout the day. I felt good about the farm and the crops for the first time, I took a pride in the nice green fields of corn that I had helped to plow and I was beginning to admire and respect the old man as a farmer.

During the wet season, the crops required a lot of work, for everything grew very fast, and the old man, always up before daylight, would walk over the fields, and when he saw the grass and weeds choking out the plants, he would wave his arms and say, 'We're lost. This crop is lost; the grass and the weeds have got it. If we can't keep up with them, we had just as well go back to town.'

Then suddenly the rains stopped and the summer sun grew hotter and heated the rocks underfoot. The air became drier and the south wind began to blow. Soon the effects of the last rain on our hill disappeared. The ground began to bake and a thin crust formed.

The old man had plowed the corn three times. Although it was only knee-high, and other farmers were waiting for the next rain, the old man continued to plow his small patch of corn on the west side regularly every eight days. 'That will hold the moisture,' he said.

But in spite of frequent plowing the moisture was soon all gone, or appeared to be, and though the corn continued to develop faster, it stopped growing, and the rich dark green gradually began to fade.

The other crops also were affected by the change in climate. Although the oats were only a few inches high, they began to head out almost overnight, and after a few weeks of the dry weather, the heads and stalks and blades of the oats began to turn yellow. The cowpeas, the peanuts, and the sorghum began to lose their rich color.

But it was in the garden where the effects of the drouth were most noticeable.

'It's the unrotted manure,' said the old man. 'It has begun to burn my garden.'

The garden began to shrivel and turn yellow. We carried water to the tomato plants and poured it into perforated cans buried beside them. They freshened up for a few hours, but the water soon disappeared into the dry, sandy soil.

That year the old man made many trips down to the corn field. After a few weeks of the dry weather the lower blades on the stalks began to turn yellow. The tops of the stalks were burned and twisted. The corn was just getting into silk and tassel and it was burning up as if it were put into an oven.

'The manure undoubtedly makes it burn much worse,' said the old man.

'You shouldn't have put it on, Brother Mac,' said Charley, who had walked down to the field with him.

'How was I to know that a six weeks' drouth was coming?' snapped the old man, who was angry that his first crop was a failure.

'Looks like the peas are going to burn up too,' said Charley, who seemed to like to irritate the old man. 'And look at them fruit trees you set out. Looks like they're dead in spite of your watering them.'

'More labor lost,' I thought.

We had worked early and late taking care of those trees. The old man had laid off two acres for an orchard and set about half of it in peach, apple, cherry, pear, and plum trees. We had dug down among the rocks (the orchard spot was the rockiest on the farm) and dug a hole three feet in diameter and three feet deep. Then we had filled the excavation with rich soil and manure, and set the young tree out after filling up the hole with water.

All spring and summer my brother and I had been watering those trees. We carried water until the well went almost dry. It got so that only a few bucketfuls would run in at a time. In wet weather the well was almost full, but that summer it didn't furnish much more than enough to take care of the stock. It takes an enormous quantity of water to run a farm. The horses, the cows, all the animals drink so much; and many garden plants need a little water when a drouth comes.

Well, it got so we could only spare a few buckets of water a day for the fruit trees and after we had to stop, most of them died. The Bermuda grass the old man had set out in the yard also got sick. A lot of it looked as if it were dead, turned completely yellow. The ground on which the Bermuda was growing was mostly underlaid by rocks, so that the grass could not send its roots down very deep for moisture when a drouth came.

In spite of all the old man's efforts, in spite of all the work he had put in and the money he had spent, his crops were dying and his work had gone for nothing.

The drouth dashed our hopes as well as those of the old man. We had been teased a good deal about the farm and we wanted the first year of our work to be a big success. Now it seemed that everything was going to be a failure.

The neighbors passed by and looked at the dying fields and laughed.

One day, when we were visiting the Irwin boys, we had quite a discussion about the old man as a farmer. Fred and Gross Irwin were older than we were and they enjoyed teasing us about our rock and air farm.

'Your father is no farmer,' said Fred. 'Look at his crops. They are all burnt up.'

'It's not our fault if a big drouth comes,' replied my sister Beatrice.

'My father is as good a farmer as yours,' I said. 'He's a better farmer.'

Gross, the oldest boy, laughed. 'Look at his crops. If he had had any judgment he wouldn't have tried to farm that old pile of rocks.'

'You just wait and see. We'll make a go of this farm

yet,' I said, repeating what the old man had said word for word.

'The truth of it is,' said Gross, 'your father is a preacher, not a farmer. He doesn't know anything about farming and this crop proves it.'

'He is a better farmer than yours,' I shouted, becoming very angry because I couldn't think of any good argument to offer.

'All those rocks he's been hauling around,' continued Gross. 'What's he doing that for? What's the use of all that work? Pa says he'll never get his money back from having all those rocks moved.'

'You just wait and see. We'll make a good farm of the old hill yet,' was all we could think of to say.

But the Irwin boys just laughed.

I think a good many people must have laughed at the work of the old man that first year. Piling rocks around, as they said, was something new in that country. Nobody ever thought of moving them off the fields, much less building rock dams.

But in spite of the skepticism of the neighbors, our faith in the old man, although we didn't understand clearly what it was all about, was unshaken.

Uncle Henry came out to see us when the drouth was at its height. The old man and Charley were plowing corn for the last time and it must have been about one hundred and five in the shade.

These hot days dampened our enthusiasm for the farm. I had gotten over my first liking for it, anyway. It was play no longer. It was hard, hot work, and the hot rocks and the hot dry sandy soil burnt my feet. My big straw hat didn't seem much protection from the broiling sun.

'A man ain't got no business working in such heat,' Charley said. 'Why the old man wants to plow this corn is more than I can see. Anybody can see it's going to burn up and plowing it won't stop it.'

But, of course, he wouldn't have dared to say this to the old man. He had tried a time or two telling him how to run his farm and had got bawled out for his pains. 'That's what I get for taking an interest in this farm,' he had grumbled to us boys later.

But Uncle Henry wasn't as backward about giving advice and saying 'I told you so' as Charley.

That day, when he came down to the field, he threw it up to the old man that the place was a failure. 'Now I guess you wish you had listened to me, Jim. Anybody can see that this old drouthy hill won't make a crop.'

'Now you never mind with your "I told you so's,"' replied the old man, who had stopped his horse in the shade of the persimmon tree in the lower end of the field. 'There's more ways of killing a dog than choking it on butter. Of course, I didn't expect much of a crop this year. This old washed-out land won't stand a drouth yet, but you just wait and see. I'll build it up and fill it full of humus, then it will hold the moisture better. Besides, this is an unusually dry summer. With a good season I would have made a fair crop even with the land as poor as it is.'

'Jim, you beat anybody I ever saw,' said Uncle Henry. 'You get an idea into your head and there's no getting it out. You can't change this climate and you can't change this hill.'

'I'll change this hill and you will live to see I'm right. Give me five years and you'll see I'm right. There's no use talking to you about it, I guess. All I can say is, just wait five years.'

Uncle Henry shook his head sadly. He knew it was no use to try to convince the old man he had been wrong on anything.

'I believe it'll rain in a day or two, Henry,' continued the old man. 'You see those clouds over there in the southeast.'

'Well, I hope so, Jim. A rain might save the cowpeas, though I'm afraid the corn's about gone now.'

Every night it would cloud up a little and sometimes there was lightning in the west and some wind from the east, but no rain came.

We grew to hate those tantalizing threats of rain. We knew that it seldom came from the east, but we couldn't help hoping when it clouded up in that direction. We had been taught that it was good to pray for those things that we needed. When we had prayers, all of us asked the Lord to send a rain for our dying crops.

'O Lord,' prayed the old man, 'if it please Thee and if it is in accord with Thy plans, send us a good gully-washer. We have worked hard, O Lord, and have followed Thy will to the best of our knowledge, and we beseech Thee to send us a rain so that we may enjoy the fruits of our labor.'

We had prayers on the farm every night. It was another of our family customs. All of us said a little prayer, and although most of us children's prayers were a mumbo-jumbo, thanking the Lord for providing for us, and asking him to bless each member of the family, and forgive us our sins, the old man's prayers were made to fit every occasion. If it rained too much, he asked that the Lord close the heavens so we could get out of the grass, and if we needed a rain, he asked the Lord to send, not a little shower that would settle the dust, but a gully-washer. 'Open up the heavens wide, O Lord, and let the water come down by the bucketful. We don't want to lose our crops, O Lord. We want Thee to make our hill green again.'

It seemed to me that the Lord was singularly careless about the rains and often deaf to the entreaties of the old man. Of course, it always rained eventually, but the percentage of good responses to the old man's pleas was remarkably low. In Oklahoma the Lord would either send too much rain or not enough.

We never questioned, at least not aloud, the efficacy of prayer. We often wondered, though, why the old man usually (at least in matters of the weather) got the opposite of what he asked.

My mother gave us an interpretation that satisfied us for the time being. 'God often tries His people,' she explained. 'He sends us trials and sorrows to test our faith. There are many cases in the Scripture where He has done this. He even took away a man's child once. You remember how He had Abraham take Isaac out to make a sacrifice of him.'

We were more concerned, however, by the way the drouth affected the old man than in any theological interpretations. He was very unhappy and gruff. He walked over the burning fields many times, looking first at the clear sky with never a sign of a cloud in the west where he expected the rain to come from.

Once, when the sun finally retreated behind the horizon, having burned the field all day relentlessly, he shook his great fist at it in silent rage.

Sometimes he grumbled: 'Always setting clear, never a cloud. Oh, why doesn't the Lord send rain for these crops before they perish?'

But the Lord continued to turn a deaf ear.

Toward the end of the drouth, about the last of July, the old man and I took a long walk clear around that twenty acres. It was just about a year from the time we had taken our first walk over the place, and I remember that the scene of desolation was much the same as it had been then.

True, there were some changes. There was the big eight-room painted house and there were some new fences. There was an air of tidiness about the place that had not existed before, but the condition of the crops was about the same.

The gully was still there and, although there were a few dams of rocks built across it, it was almost as deep as ever. The year before, on either side of it there had been stunted cotton and corn, but now there were dwarfish oats burnt to a crisp by the sun and the hot south wind.

The old man didn't say much. He just growled and sputtered when he looked at the burning fields and when he looked at the gully.

'I am ruined,' he said. 'Ruined! World without end!'

He stood so long looking at the field and the big gully that I finally slipped away. The rocks were burning my bare feet so much that cold shivers ran up and down my back.

But the old man continued to stand on the brow of the hill and look down on the ruined crops below.

6

MRS. McDONALD, YOU STICK TO YOUR POTS AND PANS

THE old man had broken down a lot of the reticence of the Badger Lee people because he had for years worked among the Cherokees. The old men and old women knew him and gave him their silent approval; they asked him to their homes and entertained him with the best that they had.

But my mother's relationship to the Badger Lee community was different. She had not gone with the old man on his jaunts into the backwoods. Consequently she was unknown to the people and looked down on as a city woman and a foreigner.

When we first moved out to the hill, we changed our Sunday habits. Formerly we had gone to the Sunday School at Sallisaw, but now we went every week to the Badger Lee schoolhouse.

The first time the old man preached there he announced that there would be Sunday School the next week, but nobody showed up except a gang of boys who gathered in the yard under the big oak trees.

'Looks like our Sunday School isn't going to be successful,' said my mother ruefully after we had cleaned the place up and waited for quite a while. 'Well, children,' she said to Beatrice, Worden, and me, 'we'll have it by ourselves.' So we got out our quarterlies and read the assignment over; then we answered the questions and had discussion and prayer.

The next Sunday was a little better. Aunt Sally McCoy and her daughter Peachy came out, and some of the Adair women. My mother had called on them and a number of others during the week and they had all promised to help her get a Sunday School started. Attendance improved a little after that, but it continued to be very low all that first year, except for the once a month when the old man preached.

One of the reasons that people wouldn't come out was that the organ was broken. It would play, but only in a wheezy, half-hearted manner. Some of the community toughs had pulled some of the keys out and jammed whiskey bottles in behind the keyboard.

'What we need, Aunt Sally,' said my mother, 'is a new

organ. If we had one, I believe more of the young people would come out.'

'That's right, Sister Mac,' replied Aunt Sally. 'I was just a-tellin' Peachy we need a new organ, we sure do.'

Aunt Sally was one of the few women in the community that had become friendly with my mother. Charley McCoy, her husband, was one of the old man's best friends. Although he could never get him out to church, he admired him because he was a good hard-working farmer. Charley had one of the best bottom-land farms in the country. He was one of the few Indians to get good land in his allotment. He hung on to it too.

A lot of the Indians sold their land and drank up the money, but not Charley. 'Charley McCoy is one of the best providers in the community,' said the old man. 'You will always find meat in his smokehouse, and his wife makes some of the best fried chicken I ever tasted.'

Poor Boy, as everybody called him, was the son of Aunt Sally and Charley McCoy, and he was quite different from his father. He had sold his land the day he was twenty-one, and had spent the money. He liked to drink and to gamble, but he was one of the best-hearted Indian bucks in the community. Although Aunt Sally spoke good English and Charley's English was pretty fair, Poor Boy never learned to speak it very well. I think he had associated with full-bloods most of his life and he had picked up their speech characteristics.

Poor Boy always greeted us in the most friendly way. 'Hello, Annus. Hello, Werna. How goes, what going on?'

Poor Boy, as far as I know, never got inside the church house. He usually came and stayed in the front yard and sometimes raced his horse by the windows when the service was going on.

'Maybe we could have a pie supper and raise some money for an organ, Sister Mac,' said Aunt Sally.

'Now that's a good idea, Mrs. McCoy,' replied my mother. 'That may be the solution.'

So my mother and Aunt Sally and a few other women of the community made their plans. At the next church service she had the old man announce it and all the girls were asked to bring pies to sell. The money was to go into a new organ.

The pie supper was held on the following Saturday night and Cebe Philips auctioned off the pies. Cebe was one of the best auctioneers and story-tellers in the community. He lived over near Price's Chapel where Uncle Green and Aunt Jennie lived and he came over to help the Badger folks out.

All the girls were there in their best clothes, with their eyes out for the boys. That was one of the attractions of a pie supper. The boy who was setting up to a girl would bid on her pie and get to eat it with her. Of course, no one was supposed to know which pie was which, but the girls could recognize the package that the pies were wrapped up in and they would give the boy friend the wink to let him know. Sometimes several boys would get to bidding against each other and the price of the pie went away up. The prettier the girl the more the boy would pay. Once in a while there'd be a good deal of feeling worked up over these contests.

This night there was quite a bit of competition, with the result that several pies sold for five or six dollars. The money-raising campaign was a big success. Over eighty dollars was turned over to Argus Hemstetter to go to town and buy a new organ with.

'Well, that's a great relief off my mind,' said my mother, going home in the buggy that night. 'That pie supper solved the problem. We should have a new organ next Sunday.'

A few days later, Poor Boy McCoy came riding up to our place. 'Hello, Annus. Hello, Annus,' he said, getting off his horse. 'Woman home?'

'Why, yes, Poor Boy. She's on the back porch churning. Why?'

'News, news about organ money,' said Poor Boy, who always spoke in monosyllables.

I called to my mother.

'Hello, Poor Boy,' greeted my mother. 'Won't you come in?'

'Old woman said to tell you Argus done stole organ money. Left country.' And without another word he turned on his heel and walked to his horse that was standing in the front yard, mounted, and galloped away.

The loss of the organ money was quite a blow to us all, my mother especially. She wasn't anywhere near getting the Sunday School at Badger started, and she had counted on the success of this organ project to bring together the people and break down some of the rural and Indian reserve. The Indians were good friends once you got their confidence, but that took a long time.

The incident aroused so much indignation in the community, however, that some of the people got together on their own initiative and began raising money to buy some kind of organ. The old man had a big hand in this and due to his efforts they got together enough for a second-hand organ so that in a few weeks after the money was stolen we had music for church and Sunday School.

My mother played the organ, and although she was not an experienced player and the new second-hand organ was a bit wheezy, the music was pretty good and a few people began coming out to Sunday School regularly. The ladies of the community grew more friendly and we began to get numerous invitations to dinner, which was a sign that we were accepted in the little Cherokee Indian community.

On Sundays that the old man preached at Dwight or Price's Chapel he left early, riding Nell. The rest of us went to Badger in the buggy. We usually drove Star, who was much gentler than Nell, but was inclined to be a little slow and poky. The old man soon found that two horses were not enough to run a farm, so he bought a young fiery colt from Mr. Cassidy, the neighbor who owned the place just to the north of us.

Before he closed the deal for Dude, my mother came out to the front porch where they were talking. She knew that the old man was thinking of using Dude for a buggy horse and, having had sad experiences with un-trained colts before, she was anxious to know if he had been broken.

'Is Dude afraid of trains?' she asked Mr. Cassidy.

The old man and Mr. Cassidy went on talking. When my mother repeated the question, the old man turned to her and said: 'Mrs. McDonald, you stick to your pots and pans. I am managing this deal.'

So she turned and went into the house.

The colt seemed rather gentle most of the time and the old man thought it would be safe for us to drive him to Badger. The next Sunday I hooked Dude up to the buggy.

We made it to the schoolhouse without any mishap, but coming home we met a car and Dude shied away from it to one side of the road.

I was driving and held him down all right until a piece of paper which was caught on the barbed-wire fence began rattling and blowing in the wind. This scared Dude so much that he started off at a gallop. He had a tough mouth and I was unable to hold him. But I was keeping him on the road, and everything would have been all right if my mother hadn't tried to help out. She got excited and reached over my hands, pulling on the lines as hard as she could. She had had rheumatism in one of her arms and her strong arm pulled Dude into the fence. The left-hand hub caught on a post and brought the buggy to a sudden halt. Both my mother and I flew over the dashboard without touching it, and right under the feet of the plunging horse. He was jerked down on top of me and mashed my knee and hip.

Strangely enough, my mother wasn't hurt much, only skinned up a little. The excited horse broke away from the buggy. The impact had torn the traces loose from the single-tree and Dude ran down the road dragging the harness after him. One of the neighbors happened to be passing by and caught him and brought him back. He patched up the harness and hooked the colt back up and drove us home. Dude was now as gentle as a lamb.

My mother telephoned for Doctor Morrow and he came

out and examined my leg and said I would be all right in a few days.

When the old man got home that night from Dwight, we told him about the incident and he almost exploded. He was sure it was the car that caused Dude to run away, although we told him it was the wind blowing the paper.

'These cars,' he said, 'are ruining the country in more ways than one. They are not only bankrupting the country; now they are killing my wife and children by scaring the horses. I tell you it's not safe to drive in the public highways any more. I ought to sue that fellow who drove the car that scared Dude. Yes, I ought to sue him.'

My mother kept insisting that it was not the car that caused the horse to run away, but he paid no attention.

Sunday School and church work took up only a small part of my mother's time. She had a thousand and one things to do on the farm. She worked early and late getting a flock of chickens started, cooking, cleaning, canning, preserving, and taking care of the house and our clothes.

Now that the old man had his farm, he worked from daylight to after dark. He was apt to forget — indeed he scarcely realized in the first place — that children needed a little encouragement and reward; that all work and no play will make Jack not only a dull boy but an unhappy one. Whenever there was a task assigned to us children that was too much for us, whenever the old man worked us too hard and deprived us of pleasures, my mother was always there to lighten the work or shorten the hours a little; or to beg him to allow us some little excursion or outing, like going to a circus, a picnic, or a barbecue.

Not that she was always successful. The old man looked

upon many modern forms of amusement as instruments
of the Devil.

I remember quite vividly the time she tried to get him
to let us go to a picture show. She argued that this was
all right for us to see because it was about the crucifixion
of Christ.

But the old man was adamant. 'It makes no difference,'
he said. 'These children are not going to a moving picture.
I am not so naïve as you, Mrs. McDonald. I am not taken
in by any of these modern tricks. Oh, I remember a
preacher friend and I went to one of these religious shows
in San Antonio, Texas, when I was a pastor there, and
right in the middle of the picture some almost naked
women came dancing out. They didn't have as much on
them as a picked goose. If the children want to learn about
the crucifixion, let them study the Bible.'

During those early years on the farm it was not often
that such discussions about pleasure took place. We were
far too busy, and my mother most of all, to try to convince
the old man of the necessity of pleasure.

That first year my mother began building up a big flock
of chickens. Taking care of chickens is a never-ending job.
Although my mother raised them in the old-fashioned
way, she had numerous difficulties. At the beginning of
the second year she set about half of the two dozen hens.
She used the back room of the old cabin for a setting-hen
house.

It was a source of amazement to me and my brother and
sister that the hens would sit on the eggs for the three
weeks that it took for the little chicks to hatch out. We
used to go out and feed them once a day and they would

get off the nests and gobble up some food hastily, take a drink of water, and hop back on the nests, where they would sit twenty-four hours more without moving.

Then when the chicks finally pecked their way out of their prisons, we were further amazed by the care the old hen took of her little ones. Frequently, she showed an antipathy toward chicks not her own, pecking them savagely, but feeding and looking out for her own brood constantly.

If hawks approached — and they often did — she burst out with a shrill warning and gathered her chickens under her protecting wings or taught them to run to the shelter of the porch or the barn. Then, if the hawk swooped down to sink its sharp claws into the back of some exposed chick, the hen would sally forth to do battle. A good alert hen can beat off a small hawk any day.

Many people lost chickens from hawks in those days, especially those who used the new-fangled brooders, which are no protection against chicken hawks.

Occasionally, however, we lost a few chickens from hawks. The old man got out the twelve-gauge shotgun and killed a few of them, although most of the birds were too clever to get within gunshot.

That second year we had about a hundred and fifty fine young chickens — Rhode Island Reds and white Leghorns mostly. When they were all out pecking at the Bermuda or in the rye patch, they were as pretty a bunch of chickens as ever I saw.

Then something began to happen to them. One by one they began to disappear. My mother did not notice it at first because she was so busy with other things, but soon she noticed that one hen who had eighteen chickens to begin with now had only twelve. 'It must be the rats,' she said.

We kept the hens and their broods in the little side room where they were hatched. About dark they would call their broods together and go to bed, each hen hovering her own chickens. We shut the outside door at night to keep out skunks and other varmints.

My mother examined the little room, and sure enough there were holes there with feathers that showed signs of rats carrying off chickens. Then one morning we found one little chicken dead and there was blood on the mother hen. The hen had evidently fought off the rats, but not before they had killed the chicken.

'Something has got to be done,' my mother said. 'At this rate all our chickens will soon be eaten by those nasty rats.'

The old man was called in, and he got me and Charley to build some little chicken coops out of one-inch boards. Each one was big enough to hold a hen and her brood, and there was a door which could be closed snugly when they were safely inside. We had quite a time getting the chickens to live in their new homes. Sometimes we had to run the hen down and put her in by force. Or we tolled them in by feed. After a while, however, they went to their new coops of their own accord.

We had one more piece of bad luck with the chickens that year. Next to rats and hawks, the biggest danger to them is those heavy spring rains. Young chickens are very foolish and will not get into the dry during a shower. Sometimes they ignore the warning of the old hen and stay

out in the rain or wander out of earshot of their mother.
If the rain is very hard, they are apt to be drowned.

We had a very violent storm that spring that laid out
fifty or sixty of our little chickens. After it was over, we
went out and picked them up. A few showed signs of life.

'Carry them in and put them on the kitchen stove,' my
mother said.

We had a big range with a great warming place on the
back side. We laid out the little chickens on this place
on a cloth and in a few minutes some of them began to
flutter and show other signs of life. All afternoon and way
into the night we worked with the chicks drying them out
and keeping them warm until they thoroughly recovered.
We revived all of them except ten or fifteen who were too
far gone to recover. My mother worked over each chicken
as arduously as if it were a newborn baby. She wrapped
it in warm cloths until it came to, and then kept the whole
bunch in the kitchen all night, keeping a fire going so they
wouldn't catch cold.

Their mothers were in a dither because their chickens
were gone. They ran around the yard aimlessly, clucking
and sputtering, calling to their lost ones.

'That's what you get for not taking better care of your
children,' my mother said. 'You don't deserve to have
any chickens.'

At last the job of saving the chickens was done, and our
flock, though reduced a little, still was the finest in the
community. Soon we were having fried chicken several
times a week. My mother saved all the pullets except the
scrubby ones.

'Next year we will have a fine young bunch of hens,'
she said.

7

NEVER LAY A LINE OVER ANY OF
MY STOCK AGAIN

BECAUSE of the drouth the crops were ruined the first
year. The rain finally came, but it came too late. Most
of the fruit trees were dead, the oats were not worth
cutting, and the other crops were cut short.

But you would not think from the way the old man
worked that he had experienced a failure. Even while
the drouth was in full swing he went ahead with his plans.
Most farmers rest in the shade during hot weather; that
is, unless there is harvesting to do. But not the old man.
He set about having another well dug so he would have

enough water in another dry spell. He cleared new ground, saying that the best time to cut sprouts was in hot weather. He killed all the weeds he could to limit next year's growth.

'There are two things I hate besides sin,' he said, 'and they are dog fennel and cockleburs. Why the Lord made them, I don't know, unless it was to punish sinners. Anyway, I don't see why we good people have to put up with them.'

A lot of our time was spent at the hot, unpleasant job of pulling them up.

Farm life turned out to be a little bit different from what we had expected. Before we had moved out to the hill, we all had rosy dreams of horseback riding, making money, and eating all the good things we raised. Now we were not enjoying many of these things and we found we had to work very hard.

Even my brother Worden, who was only six, had his tasks. The old man put him to pulling weeds, picking up rocks, or sent him on errands. I had to work harder — to pull sprouts or hoe corn or do other tasks requiring more judgment.

Often Worden, being only a child, would forget what he was supposed to do, but the old man would insist that he complete the task he was assigned.

'He's just a baby, Mr. McDonald. You can't expect him to work,' said my mother.

But the old man would say, 'No such thing. He's a big boy. He can do more than Angus.'

Then Worden would throw out his little chest and work very hard for a few minutes. Soon he would forget and sit down and play or go to pulling up sweet potato plants instead of weeds and grass.

One day we were busy in the orchard piling up rocks, when Worden said, 'Papa, I have got a fever. I can't do any more.'

'Nonsense, boy,' the old man said. 'There's nothing wrong with you.'

'Oh yes,' said Worden. 'I've got a fever. I'm real sick.'

'All right, then, go to the house if you're sick.'

After Worden went to the house, the old man turned to me and Charley. 'I'll fix that rascal,' he said. 'You wait and see. I'll make him wish he'd never had a fever,' he said, laughing.

We went in to dinner and got ready to sit down to the table, after having washed our hands and faces in the washbasin. On hot days Charley got the sweat out of his hair on the towel. This made quite a stink.

Today was no exception. It was very hot and the sweat from Charley's wet hair got on the towel.

'You boys take this towel,' my mother said.

I looked around and there was Worden waiting in line to wash. The old man always washed himself first, wetting his hair and combing it while he looked in the little mirror that hung on the back porch. Then the hired hands washed next and we boys last.

Nobody ever told us to line up in this order. It was understood and was one of the many rituals that went to make up our home. It was just as important in a way as the custom of not eating until the old man had returned thanks.

Since we didn't raise cotton, my sister did not work in the field. 'The women should take care of the house and the garden,' said the old man, 'except when we get in a push.' It was one of his unwritten and unspoken laws that no woman should be required to work in the field except in cotton chopping or picking time.

The old man was very proud, though, of his own sisters' work in the field when he was a boy. 'Lu used to plow like a man, and Alice was the best cotton picker in the country,' he was never tired of repeating.

Today my brother took his place behind me to get washed up for dinner. The old man pretended not to notice him. We all went over and sat down around the big porch table.

Then the old man turned and looked at Worden, who must have been very hungry, for he kept gazing greedily at the food.

'Mother,' he said, 'why didn't you put this young man to bed? He has a fever. He got it while piling rocks in the orchard this morning.'

'Why, I didn't know he was sick,' my mother replied. 'He seemed to be feeling all right when he came to the house.'

'Did he tell you why he took out?' asked the old man.

'Oh yes, he said you said he had done enough for today. He said you said that too much work was not good for a little boy. He said you said he might be "stumped" if he worked so hard.'

'He'll be stunted all right,' said the old man, who couldn't keep from smiling. 'I'll stunt him! Now, sonny,' he said, turning to my brother, who through all this had said nothing, not knowing whether his conduct was approved or disapproved. 'Now, sonny,' repeated the old man, 'you may go up and go to bed until your fever is over. You are too sick to eat.'

'But, Papa, I don't have a fever any more,' said Worden. 'I am cured of it.'

'No. I am convinced you are a very sick boy. Mother, you'd better take him and put him to bed.'

'But I am hungry,' said my brother, bursting into tears. 'I want my dinner. I don't have a fever any more.'

In spite of this outburst the old man insisted that he be taken from the table. 'I am going to cure him of these fevers,' he said. 'Worden has been having one every few days all this summer.'

That afternoon I came back to the house about two o'clock to get some water for the old man and Charley. They were still working in the orchard trying to get the rocks piled up preparatory to hauling them out. They took the crowbar and prized the big ones out of the ground and then broke them with a sledgehammer. Some of the rocks were almost as big as a wagon bed, but they were not over five or six inches thick at the most and they were fairly easily broken.

We had a big twelve-pound sledgehammer that the old man could swing all day without getting tired. Charley was worn out when he worked beating rocks with the old man, but he never would admit it.

I drew water from the well, filled the fireless-cooker vessel which we used in the field because the water stayed cool in it a long time, then I filled the cedar bucket on the back porch. The old man had taught us never to go to the well without filling the porch water bucket, and never to pass by the woodpile without carrying in a load of wood. 'A man who won't keep his wife in wood and water is not any account,' he said.

I looked up on the back porch and saw my brother sitting up to the table. There was a nice meal laid out in front of him and he was eating as if he were starved.

'I thought Worden had a fever,' I said to my mother, who was watching the hungry boy gobble up the food.

'He is cured of his fever now,' said my mother, 'and I don't think he will have another for a long time.'

After the crops were laid by, the old man started on the gullies. He hired Dee Daggles, who was a good enough hand if you worked with him, and an old man my brother and I nicknamed 'Cleany.' We called him that for the same reason that we called Uncle Dave Daggles's living skeleton of a horse 'fatty.' Old Uncle Cleany was not much of a worker, so the old man paid him only seventy-five cents a day.

He was constitutionally opposed to taking a bath. Both the old man and my mother threw out hints about how healthful it was, and on Saturday night my mother heated a big kettle of water and set out a big tub, but he wouldn't take a bath for love or money.

Uncle Cleany never had much regard for women's judgment, though he imagined he was a great ladies' man. One time he started to tell us one of his stories about his experiences with the fair sex. 'I reckon I always was a right smart hand with the women,' he said. 'And I never fail to speak out when I take to a woman. Just like when I was chinning with the Widow Spreckles across the holler.

I says to her, I says, "Woman, I like your shape, I like your shape."'

But we didn't get to hear the rest of the story because the old man called to us. 'Come, boys, it's burning daylight. We've got work to do.'

And out to the field we would go — to pull weeds or help haul rocks.

That fall we helped gather the crops, what little there was to gather. About all the corn we got was a few little nubbins. The crop of cowpeas was better, though. We made considerable hay and we picked a lot of the peas for seed next year. On the first windy day after the peas were thoroughly dried, we piled them on a wagon sheet in the yard and beat the hulls off with two broomsticks. Then we poured them slowly in the wind so that all the chaff was blown out.

Some of the other crops were not an entire failure. There was a fair amount of Irish potatoes, which we put away in the cellar for the winter, and we had sweet potatoes and some meat in the smokehouse.

The first cold spell the old man got the neighbors to help him slaughter a couple of shotes. He smoked the meat with a hickory-chip fire for six weeks and it was dry and salty.

'I'll have to experiment a little with it,' he said, 'before I get it just the right flavor. I left it down in the salt a little too long and there was too much smoke on it.'

The fresh meat tasted good, and although our little farm was considered a failure by the neighbors, and even to some extent by ourselves, we had more to eat than when we had lived in town.

'You children just wait,' said the old man when we remarked on the improved fare. 'We'll have a lot more to eat than this in a few years.'

My mother, of course, did her share in storing up food for the winter. Although the garden was mostly burnt up and there was no fruit on the place, we managed to save the tomatoes by watering them. The result was that we had all we wanted to eat and there were several bushels for canning.

My mother worked long and hard at that. It took many hours over a hot stove before the job was done and jar after jar of tomatoes were stacked up in one corner of the dining-room. The old man insisted that she stack them there because he wanted to show off what the rock and air farm had produced the first year.

My mother had canned some other vegetables — string beans, beets, and pickles — and we had picked blackberries and had bought several bushels of apples and peaches that she had canned and preserved. Altogether we had quite a stack of canned goods, of which we were all very proud.

Thanksgiving, at our house, was almost as much of a holiday as Christmas. We had a big dinner and we didn't have to work in the field.

Already we were getting so we looked forward to those days of rest. The newness had worn off and working on the farm was not such a thrill as it had been at first. Besides, hauling manure, cleaning out stables, or picking up rocks was not very romantic. It was hard to get a thrill out of shoveling smelly manure.

The old man, however, seemed to take pleasure in all

his work. He hated to see holidays come because they put him behind. He wouldn't work on Sunday, no matter how badly he wanted to, unless, of course, the ox was in the ditch.

This Thanksgiving we had a big fat hen stuffed with dressing and a lot of other good things to eat. My mother made about a dozen pumpkin pies and other kinds of dainties, including a cake that had a dozen eggs and I don't know how much cream in it.

People nowadays don't know how to make pies and cakes. They are too tight, I guess, to put in the ingredients.

'These little bakery-store cakes,' the old man used to sneer sometimes after some church sister had given him a piece of one. 'I can wad that cake up and put it in my watch pocket, it is so spongy and full of holes.'

'If you are stingy and use a lot of substitutes in your cooking, you are not going to have a good pie or cake,' my mother said.

During this Thanksgiving dinner we were halfway through the meal when we heard a loud noise. It sounded as though somebody had fired a twenty-two rifle right in the room. My mother jumped up and went over to the canned goods which were stacked in pasteboard boxes in the corner. One of the half-gallon jars was cracked and the tomato juice was running out. 'Bless Pat!' she said. 'The tomatoes are spoiled! I must have done something wrong. Maybe I didn't get all the air out of the jars and the tomatoes fermented.'

Many of the jars were cracked wide open; in others the liquid was spewing out at the top. The tomatoes had to be thrown to the hogs.

Their loss was quite a blow to our winter supply of food. 'I'll be more careful next time,' said my mother. 'I don't see any reason why I can't can tomatoes, though I never tried it before.'

'Your mother,' said the old man later, 'being a city woman doesn't know much about canning. She will learn, though.'

That fall we spent most of our time hauling rock. The old man was trying to get enough of them out of the orchard so that he could cultivate it next year. He and Dee Daggles would each take a sledgehammer and stand on opposite sides of a 'monstrous' rock after it had been raised with crowbars and prize poles. The old man would set the pace and Dee would have to swing fast to keep from getting hit by the sledgehammer. At last, after many blows, the rock would crack. Then two men would have to throw it into the wagon. The old man did not want the rocks broken up any smaller because he said big ones were necessary to a successful dam. The water, he said, had great power and the dam must be constructed properly.

The old man started building dams in the big giant gully on the north side of the farm. The first thing he did was to take a spade and dig down the sides of the gully. Then he smoothed out the bottom so he would have a place to lay the big rocks on. He made the dam about four feet wide, and constructed it very carefully, fitting the rocks together. He would take a rock and fit it in against the others and chip it off with the sledgehammer so the sides would fit snug. He was very skillful in breaking out the rocks to just the right size.

When the rock dam was finished, the lower side was almost smooth. It rose almost perpendicular, but slanting a little back up the hill. The old man filled in back of the dam with small rocks at the bottom, then toward the top of the banks of the gully he made them larger.

This approach, as he called it, extended back a few feet, and would help break the force of the down-rushing water. We worked several days on each dam. It took us that long because the old man was so particular.

This rock-hauling was good training for the team, which was still pretty wild, especially Nell, who ran away every chance she got.

That fall Uncle Cagey, who was a distant relative and preacher, came to see us. The old man said Cagey was a good enough worker, but the worst manager you could imagine. He couldn't keep a church, his sermons were so long-winded.

'Uncle Cagey is a good man, but churn-headed,' the old man said. 'He's bookish. He'll sit down to read a book when there's not a dust of flour in the house. He works on his sermons when he ought to be thinking about keeping the smokehouse full.'

The old man said that lots more people would go to hell for not working during the week than for getting the ox out of the ditch on the Sabbath.

The winter Uncle Cagey came to visit us the old man put him to work building dams and hauling rocks.

We were using Star and Nell in the wagon and Nell was still pretty skittish. She always tried to pull all the load, and would run away at the drop of your hat. I can see her now with her head high in the air, her neck bowed, prancing along pulling two thirds of the load. The other mare, Star, we had tamed down, but we couldn't take the fire out of Nell.

The old man was usually pretty rough and impatient with stock — that is, broken stock — but he was gentle with Nell. He wouldn't use the stay chain on her; he'd unhook it so she wouldn't have to pull so much.

The old man put Uncle Cagey to work. He said the way to treat people who never knew when to leave was to give them a job. The chances were that's why they visited so much — to get out of work at home.

We had got one load of rock hauled and had begun on the second when somebody came to see the old man.

It was a cold morning and both the mares were still prancing, so the old man hated to leave the rock-hauling in charge of anyone else. He was afraid the team would run away or be overloaded or spoiled in some way. Charley was a pretty good hand with wild stock, though. So the old man said, 'Now, Charley, be careful. Watch the team and handle them just like I would.'

Uncle Cagey spoke up. 'Don't worry about this team, I'll handle 'em. I didn't spend twenty years breaking colts for nothing.'

'You let Charley handle this team,' said the old man.

We had just been hauling light loads of rock because when we started the load, Nell would lunge, and if her weight didn't move the wagon she would rear up and lunge again. She was so excitable, she was liable to do anything. The old man handled her with kid gloves. We had about got the wagon half full and Charley said, 'That ought to be enough,' but Uncle Cagey said, 'You don't mean you're

going to let that mare bluff you. Put a load on that mare
and it'll learn her to prance around.'

He went around and fastened the stay chains on Nell's
end of the double-tree. 'We'll put a load on her she'll remember. You've got to work the fire out of that mare.'

Charley argued with Uncle Cagey, but it did no good.
The old man called Uncle Cagey a churn-headed fool, and
I guess he was, all right. He'd just take charge of everything and if anybody went against him, he'd throw out his
chest and talk about how much he knew. 'Don't try to
teach your grandmother how to milk ducks,' he told
Charley.

Well, we went ahead and loaded the wagon full of rocks.
My brother and I knew Uncle Cagey was wrong, but we
were little and had been taught that children should be
seen and not heard, so we didn't say anything. When the
rock bed was full, Uncle Cagey climbed up on the seat
and braced his feet. 'Giddap, you hussies!' he hollered in
a loud voice.

That was another one of the old man's rules that he
broke. A man's voice will excite a horse quicker than anything. The old man always spoke to the horses gently,
unless they disobeyed him, and then he gave them
warning.

When Uncle Cagey yelled at the team, Nell jumped like
she was shot. She lunged forward and reared up. Because
the stay chain was fastened and because the wagon was
heavily loaded, she scarcely moved it. Uncle Cagey stood
up. 'I'll learn you, you hussy,' and using the end of the
long lines for a whip he cut Nell across the hips.

That mare simply went wild then. She lunged forward

from side to side; she reared straight up in the air. Uncle
Cagey held on to the lines and tried to calm the mare down
after it was too late.

When Nell reared up, she got one foot over the wagon
tongue and fell flat. But she was up like a flash, rearing,
plunging, doing everything but kicking. Star was getting
excited, too, and if there hadn't been such a heavy load on
the team, they would probably have run away in spite of
anything Uncle Cagey could have done.

Suddenly the old man appeared and made for Nell's
head talking to her as he came. 'Steady, now — steady,
old girl; everything is going to be all right. Whoa, girl,
whoa.' Nell was wild and wouldn't pay any attention.
But the old man kept edging up to her. She was still
plunging wildly while Uncle Cagey was holding her down
the best he could. In a minute the old man got hold of
Nell's bridle, but she lifted him clear off the ground. It
looked like her front hoofs would hit him when she reared
up. I thought the old man would be killed. He seemed
all mixed up in the harness and the horses' feet. But he
kept talking to the mare and in a minute she quit rearing
up so much. As soon as he could get his feet on the ground,
the old man began rubbing her throat and petting her.
She quieted down some more then, but she still pranced
around and champed her bit. It was cold that morning,
but Nell was in a lather. She was wet around the breeching, the backband, and the collar.

'Go get a blanket,' said the old man to me. So far he
had taken no notice of Uncle Cagey, who was standing in
the wagon, for once quiet. 'Unload that rock, Charley,
all of it.'

Uncle Cagey climbed down and started to unfasten the trace chains. 'Leave this team hooked up,' he said.

I gave the blanket to the old man and he covered Nell with it and he was careful to show it to her first and then hold back the blind on the bridle so she could see him put it on her.

'Brother Mac, aren't you going to take 'em out?' said Uncle Cagey.

But the old man didn't answer. He was still busy talking to Nell, who had become somewhat quieter, though she was still prancing up and down.

'There's no use — that mare won't work,' said Uncle Cagey.

When Charley had got the rock unloaded, the old man said, 'Now take the rock bed off.' We didn't know this was necessary, but we didn't question it, of course. The rock bed was made of heavy two-inch oak boards that weren't fastened together and could be taken off one at a time. When he had got the bed off, there was nothing left but the wagon frame.

'Now, Charley,' said the old man, 'put your shoulder to the wheel and roll the wagon a little when I lead the team forward.' The old man was still holding Nell by the bridle and he told her to step forward a bit. Nell, of course, thought the wagon was still loaded, and she lunged, but the old man held her back as much as he could and Charley rolled the wheel a bit so that she wasn't pulling anything at all. Around the field we went. The old man stopped and climbed up on the standards and drove back where we had unloaded. 'Now, Charley, put the bed back on.' When it was on, we drove around the field again.

Nell lunged a bit when she felt the added weight, but she soon quit that. When we were back again, the old man had us put a few rocks in the wagon. Then he'd drive by and have a few more put in, until the load was gradually increased to about what we had been hauling. We drove around the field nearly all day with light loads of rock.

All this time Uncle Cagey had been helping us, but the old man hadn't even spoken to him. About three-thirty the old man said, 'Well, that'll be enough for today.' We thought it was enough, too, because we hadn't had any dinner and we were nearly starved.

When we had taken the team out and got them fed, the old man went over to where Uncle Cagey was standing in the lot. 'Cagey,' he said, 'never lay a line over any of my stock again. You nearly ruined that mare.'

'I guess I better be going,' said Uncle Cagey. But the old man didn't hear him because he was walking toward the house.

8

THIS IS GOD'S EARTH

THE rock-hauling went on all winter. No matter how cold the days were the old man worked at it. Of course we children were in school at Sallisaw, but we worked afternoons and on Saturdays and during the Thanksgiving and Christmas holidays.

It was one day in December when we were filling the wagon with rock in the orchard that Judge Adair and Uncle Jack Rider came riding by. The orchard was right next to the section line that ran by our farm.

'Hi-ow-ee,' greeted Uncle Jack, clearing his throat and letting his voice trail off into an unintelligible sound. No one was able to figure out why Uncle Jack made this funny noise when he started speaking. Frequently, if he was asked a question and didn't want to answer, he would merely go 'Hi-ow-ee —' making it extra long and drawn out. Uncle Jack and the Judge were two of the old man's elders in the Badger Lee Church he had just organized.

'Howdy, Brother Mac,' greeted Judge Adair. 'I see you are making a fine farm out of this place, suh, yes suh.' Judge Adair was one of the most courteous men you ever saw.

'Hi-ow-ee,' said Uncle Jack.

'Why, hello, Uncle Jack. Hello, Judge. Get down, get down and hitch your horses.'

'Why, I guess we haven't time, Brother McDonald,' replied the Judge. 'What's the good word?'

'Oh, nothing much. I'm just doing a little extra work during the cold weather. It's too cold to do much else.'

'Good training for the boys,' said the Judge.

'Yes, Judge, I'll make farmers out of these boys yet. That's the reason I wanted to get them on the farm. A boy keeps out of trouble on the farm,' replied the old man. 'Will you be out at church next Sunday? I missed you last Sunday, Uncle Jack.'

'Hi-ow-ee,' said Uncle Jack.

'Oh, yes, I'll see that Jack gets out,' said the Judge. 'Well, we should be moving on. Come, go with us.'

'Oh, don't rush off,' replied the old man. 'Get down and stay awhile.'

'No. Haven't got time. You come with us,' said the Judge.

'Hi-ow-ee — come home with us,' chimed in Uncle Jack.

'No, no,' replied the old man, who suddenly thought of
Dee and Charley and Cleany, who were enjoying the rest.
They had stopped work just as soon as the old man
started talking. 'We've got to get back. It's burning
daylight.'

'Better come with us,' replied the Judge as he gathered
up the reins and clucked to his horse.

'Hi-ow-ee —' said Uncle Jack as they rode off down the
road.

'The Judge,' said the old man, 'is one of the cleverest
men I've ever known. Uncle Jack is clever too, but I
can't get him out to church. I thought when I made him
elder he'd come. But the nearest he comes is the yard of
the schoolhouse.'

The old man was having a hard time getting these
country churches started. There was too much wickedness
in the country. In the Badger community a man was considered funny-turned if he didn't drink. Frequently while
the old man was preaching inside the schoolhouse there
was a crap game going on outside. The boys and men
would congregate under the trees on Sunday and gamble
and drink and cuss when they ought to have been inside
worshiping the Lord. Oh, it was a wicked community, all
right. But the people were good-hearted, anyway. We
always got a lot of invitations to Sunday dinner. In spite
of the old man's red-hot hell-fire sermons, he was well liked.

The people seemed to like to be told they were going to
hell, and then they went right on sinning the same old way.

Sunday at our house was not only a day of rest, but it
was a day of worship. The old man was very strict about

it. He believed that the day should be spent in prayer, reading and studying the Bible. Every other family in the community went fishing or swimming, or went on an outing on Sunday, but the old man didn't allow his family to do any of these things.

I remember one time the Irwin boys came over to see us on Sunday afternoon and we were playing a jumping game in the back yard.

The old man came out and saw us. 'Boys, boys,' he said as he came up, 'stop that jumping. That is not the Lord's work. You boys come up on the porch and study your Sunday-School quarterly. I'll venture to say that none of you know your lesson for next week.'

'Well, I guess we'd better go,' said Fred. And they went home and didn't come back to see us any more on Sunday.

'None of my daddy's boys ever went swimming on Sunday, said a cuss-word or took a chew of tobacco,' he would say. He was very proud of the Puritanism of the McDonald family.

He didn't believe in Sunday games of any kind and he frowned on all card games. My mother got us some Bible card games and there was quite a crisis about whether we should play these games on Sunday or, for that matter, whether we should play them at all.

'What are those things you have got there?' he said one Sunday afternoon when my mother was showing us this new game.

'This is a Bible game,' replied my mother.

'Cards are cards, and I don't want my children playing cards,' said the old man.

My mother took them and showed him how the game

would actually teach us Bible history and he finally consented to let us play, although he always looked a little askance at the cards, particularly if we played on the front porch where people could see us.

'People passing along the road will see the preacher's children playing cards,' he said. 'You and your games,' he told my mother, 'will undermine my position in the community. You'll ruin me,' he said dramatically. 'I'll be ruined here in my own house.'

To such outbursts my mother would say nothing. She already considered that she had won the initial victory and she would try to change the subject.

On Sunday afternoons my mother educated and entertained us in other ways. Charles Dickens was her favorite author, and not long after we moved to the farm she purchased a whole set of his works.

Many a Sunday afternoon she spent in reading to us. Much of our early interest in literature was engendered by this reading.

The old man couldn't find fault with books, but he did sneer occasionally at my mother's interest and later at my interest in literature. 'I don't see any use in reading stories,' he said. 'Why don't you read history and biography?' He always considered me, for some reason, the one in the family who would be a scholar.

He had dozens of history books in his library. I followed both the encouragement of my mother and the old man. At an early age I read all the fiction books I could get hold of and all the historical and religious books in the old man's library, even the sacred encyclopedias and commentaries.

The Sunday after we saw Uncle Jack and Judge Adair was the day for the old man to preach at Badger. Although it was a day of worship and rest we had to get up early just the same, to milk and feed and get ready for Sunday School. Already we boys were milking. The old man insisted that we learn that right from the start.

'The woman of the house should not have to cut wood or milk. A man who lets his wife do either one is no account.'

So my brother and I got up early and fed the horses six ears of corn apiece, a bait of pea hay, and milked Buttercup, the young heifer that the old man had bought.

She proved to be a good buy. She gave three gallons and a half on her first calf and was one of the best-natured cows I ever knew. No matter how hard we pinched her tits she never kicked at us, though sometimes she did wince a little and look around at us reproachfully.

After we had fed and milked, we had breakfast, and then we put the stock in the pasture.

We always greased the buggy every week whether it was needed or not. The old man seemed to think as much of the buggy as he did one of his horses.

We had to black our shoes, as the old man said. He kept a box of blacking which wouldn't shine anything and he used it on his own shoes and insisted everybody else do the same, even my mother.

It was the old man's custom to get dressed in his black bow-tie and stiff-starched white shirt and best black frock-tailed suit, and then go out and hitch up Star to the buggy and yell at my mother that she was going to make him late for an appointment.

This Sunday was typical. He got ready, hitched up Star, and tied her to the big hickory tree by the house. Then he went to the foot of the stairs and yelled, 'Mrs. McDonald, are you ready?' It was two hours yet until Sunday-School time, but the old man invariably got in a swivet, no matter how early he was. Of course my mother had a lot of work to do in the house — chickens to feed and perhaps a churning to do, so the old man was always ready first.

He did nothing on Sunday — just got up about six and took a cold bath. He bragged that he had not missed gargling salt water or taking a cold bath in forty years. Then he went into his study and went over his sermon for the day. He usually wrote out his sermon the night before, but he never paid any attention to his manuscript when he was preaching.

In his study were pictures of all the great preachers, Doctor Cooper, Doctor Worden, Doctor Calhoun, and others, and of other great men, William Jennings Bryan, Theodore Roosevelt, and Thomas Jefferson. In the big cases that lined the walls were many books. There were several sets of encyclopedias and sacred commentaries, all kinds of religious histories, biographies of great religious leaders, and other religious books. There were many American histories and biographies of great Americans, and there was Ridpath's *History of the World* and the *World's History and Its Makers*. But there were no fiction books, novels, or books of poetry.

This morning, as usual, he started yelling at my mother about eight-thirty. After a little while he went down, got into the buggy, and started to drive off, calling out, 'Mrs.

McDonald, if you don't come pretty soon, I'm going to leave you.' And then he would begin shouting, 'Halloo, halloo! Are you coming?'

He yelled so loud the Irwins, who lived half a mile away, could hear him.

Then there would come my little mother — with her best hat on crooked and the powder not on straight. You could see she had just dabbed it on at the last minute. When the old man saw her coming, he said, 'Hurry, hurry, you're making me late for my appointment. I have been preaching for forty years and I've never been late yet.' And my mother, walking just as fast as she could, would break into a trot just before she came to the buggy, to appease the old man. This sort of thing happened with little variation every Sunday that the old man preached at Badger. On other weeks he took me with him to Dwight or he went alone.

After my mother had sunk back into the little buggy exhausted, the old man resumed his normal course, which was to talk about the crops and the land. Occasionally he would stop the horse in order to get a good look at some 'dirt,' as he called it. He would get out and walk out into a field and kick up the fresh earth.

Finally we arrived at Badger, the five of us — my brother and I riding horseback on Nell and the old man and my mother and sister in the buggy.

The schoolhouse where we had church lay at the foot of Badger Mountain. It was a large two-room house where they had school during the week. A gang of boys and men were clustered on the south side of the building out of the wind. Uncle Jack was among them. The old man

drove into the yard and hitched Star to a tree. Then he
went into the house. The floor was littered with paper
and trash. My mother got a broom and cleaned it up
for the services. By the time she had finished, some people
had arrived, including Judge Adair and his family. The
Judge was the superintendent of the Sunday School and
one of the pillars of the church. Soon the front room was
almost full. Most of the crowd were women and children.

There were a few boys in the back who kept walking in
and out, their spurs clanking loudly. The old man started
the church service by leading the first song, and a few of
the brothers and sisters joined in. My mother played the
new second-hand organ.

Joe Morris was sick and was not there to lead the singing. He was one of the best singers we had at Badger Lee.
Sometimes it took him a long time to get his voice un-
wound, though. I guess he did it to get the young folks
warmed to the right pitch. He usually began with "'Tis
the Old-Time Religion' and he started singing almost
under his breath, "'Tis the — 'Tis the — 'Tis the' — each
time until finally on about the twentieth "'Tis the' he
boomed out, throwing his arms up, and putting all his
strength into the song: "'Tis the old-time religion and it's
good enough for me,' until he shook the rafters. Joe was
good on the sweet-and-low songs too, like 'Shall We
Gather At the River?' and 'Rock of Ages,' that helped
push a sinner over the line when the Devil was hanging
on to his coat tails.

The old man's voice boomed out loud and strong, but
completely out of tune.

'Your Papa,' my mother said, 'can't carry a tune in a

basket, though he thinks he is the best singer in the world.'

After the singing, the old man started to preach and he took for his text the care of the soil. I don't remember what the verse was or where he got it. But I do remember that he rebuked the farmers in the congregation for raising cotton and abusing the land.

' ... This is God's earth and you are desecrating his work when you plow up and down the hill and let the water wash away the soil that the Lord has put here for our use. A lot of you people have got the idea that you can come here on Sunday and look pious and act pious and everything is fine. Everything is wonderful, you think. I went to church. I discharged my duty and I can go home and let my land go to rack and ruin. I can let my family starve. I can let my wife do the work. And let me tell you right now, the Lord loves and appreciates the good women of this community. The good women, I say, who look after the crops and milk the cow, while you trifling men are off drunk when you ought to be in the field. Some of you men are like a man I once knew back in Mississippi when I was a boy.

'*Oh yes*, this was a good man. He went to church on Sunday, but during the week he was sitting around town wearing out the seat of his pants. And he thought he was a good man. I was a boy at the time and I remember my grandfather was the pastor at Tupelo, Mississippi, and what did he say to this man who was so pious — he led in prayer, he taught in Sunday School. *What did he say!* He faced him down in front of the whole congregation. He said, "*You are the greatest sinner of them all. Do you think the Lord approves of you? You are bound as straight for hell as an Indian can shoot an arrow!*" Yes, he shamed this man in front of the congregation, but let me tell you, it was the best thing that ever happened. And do you know what happened? Why, that man came to my grandfather in open church and publicly thanked him. Yes, he thanked him because the preacher had opened his eyes. He said, "I'm going to take care of my family. I am going to milk the cows and cut the wood." Yes, that's what he said. And the Lord was pleased.

'And let me tell you, brothers and sisters! I'm going to tell you a few things like my grandfather told his people. *You people are not going to heaven! Why, you are going to hell so fast that you wouldn't travel any faster if you were in one of those new-fangled gasoline buggies. You are going straight to hell! And why?* Because you are too abominably lazy to work and take care of your crops and your families. You have got no right to abuse God's earth, and you have got no right to neglect your wife and children. *Let me tell you one thing! I'll say of my grandfather who is now in glory, praise be the Lord! Praised be his holy name!* I'll say one thing — my grandfather always kept his crops clean, and meat in his smokehouse. You would always find that he kept his wife in wood and water, and he always kept a few chickens and pigs to keep the wolf away from the door.

'*What do you think my grandfather would say about this community?* Why, let me tell you, the other day I rode my mare all over the country. I rode almost to Dwight and I took a big circle around Badger, and I looked at all the farms along the way, and I did not see a cow or a chicken or a pig or the sign of a garden anywhere. *What kind of farming is this? What kind of treatment are you giving your families and God's earth by raising nothing but cotton? Well, you can't eat cotton!* "Oh yes," you say, "but I've got to raise cotton to get money." And what do you do with your money? You go to town and buy stuff you should raise on the farm. You live out of a paper sack and you don't live half as well as you would if you raised feed crops, a garden, and livestock.

'Oh, I know a few of you men do better. A few of you men are good providers. A few of you have chickens. And when I go for dinner to your houses the table is heavy-laden with good things raised right on the farm. And if you look in the cellar you'll find jar after jar of canned fruit put away for the winter and you'll find potatoes and other good things to eat stored away. And your barns are full. And your cattle are fat. And your wives are happy. And I tell you, brothers and sisters, when I go into a home like that, I say, *Praise be the Lord! Praise on highest! Praised be his Holy Name! For this is God's work. This is God's earth and God's people and not the work of the Devil! . . . No, it is not the work of the Devil. When the Devil sees a home like that, I imagine he sticks his tail between his legs and slinks away! . . .* Let us pray!'

After the prayer there were two more songs, before the old man dismissed the congregation.

After the service the elders gathered around and shook the old man's and my mother's hands and asked us to dinner.

'Thank you,' replied the old man. 'But we are going over to Green's for dinner today, I believe.'

Uncle Green was there with his wife, Aunt Jennie.

Their house was a big log one with an open hallway running through the center. We had a fine dinner. Aunt Jennie complained that she didn't have much to eat. 'May was sick and I didn't have time to fix much,' she said. We sat down to the big long table in front of the open fireplace. There were ten or fifteen different kinds of vegetables and fruits, besides fresh pork chops, a big platter of fried chicken, some fried quail, and a roasted possum cooked with sweet potatoes.

'I guess we can make out,' said the old man, helping himself to some of the possum. 'There's nothing better than possum when it's cooked with sweet potatoes.'

We ate for an hour and you couldn't miss anything on the table. Besides our family of five, there was Uncle Green's family of four boys and two girls.

After dinner the old man and Uncle Green talked. 'You were a little sharp in your sermon today, Jim. You know these poor farmers can't get along without raising cotton.'

'Maybe so,' replied the old man, 'but I didn't give them as much as they needed. This country is going to rack and ruin because of trifling farmers. Look at your table. Why, you raise everything you eat. But you are very exceptional. Most of these farmers haven't got a cow or a pig or a chicken on the place.'

9

CAN'T YOU SEE THE OX IS IN
THE DITCH?

THE long winter finally ended and our hill became green again. This time the old man had got a head start on his farming. Although he and the hands had hauled many loads of rocks and had built dams about thirty feet apart all the way up the slope, he had found time to do other things.

In the fall he had cleaned out all the stables and scattered the manure over the garden spot and the land he intended to put in corn. Then he had turned it under, saying that it would rot and become a part of the soil so that it wouldn't burn the crop if a drouth came.

This year he planted his corn early. 'I'll get the jump on the drouth this time,' he said. He set out more fruit trees, getting new plants from Fort Smith. He improved the place in other ways, built a new tool shed and some new fences, and made gates between the fields, lots, and pastures.

Mr. Cassidy, the neighbor who owned the place to the north of us, said he never saw so many gates in his life. There were a hog pasture, a cow pasture, and several small fields, each fenced off.

That spring the old man put in a field of peanuts, another of cowpeas, and another of artichokes. 'I'll let the hogs gather their own feed,' he said. 'When the crop matures, I'll just turn the shotes in.'

When we first moved out, Mr. Irwin had given the old man a young sow. The first time the sow got in heat we loaded her into the wagon and took her over and bred her to Woodrow Wilson. Woodrow Wilson was Uncle Green's male. His boys had named him that because they thought President Wilson was the greatest man in the world.

Matilda, the sow, gave birth to ten pigs in the spring. She wasn't a big sow, but she sure could hold a lot of pigs. 'They're fine healthy Pole and China stock too,' said the old man.

Buttercup, the cow, came fresh that spring. It was a fine heifer calf, and soon she was giving four gallons a day. She never did give under three, even just before her calf came. We tried to turn her dry because the milk is not supposed to be good just before a cow comes fresh, but she just kept pouring out the milk.

'It was a lucky day when I bought that heifer,' the old man said. He gave her the best food and took care of her as he would a newborn colt. On cold nights he put a blanket over her and made a nice bed of straw in her stall. Buttercup was the old man's pride and joy. She was a fine cow — one of the finest red Jerseys I ever saw.

Other animals were giving birth too. Both the mares had been bred to the best blood in the country. Star had a colt shortly after we had moved out. Only one service was necessary. She took the Agent stud without any trouble and in a few months her belly began to swell. But Nell wouldn't stick. She would get in heat, and by the time we'd get her to the stallion she'd be out of the notion and fight the stud like a hyena, or else if he covered her, it wouldn't do any good.

The result was that Nell's colt was almost a year later than Star's. I was the oldest boy, so the old man said I could have my choice of the colts. Star's colt was a slick, pretty little fellow, with a very high temper. He'd lay back his ears and kick you without warning. I wanted Selim, but the old man bragged on Nell so much that I thought I'd wait and see what her colt looked like before I finally decided.

One morning I went down to the lot and saw a little scrawny thing standing by Nell. It wasn't quite day and I couldn't see well, but I knew Nell's colt had come at last. As it got lighter I got a good look at it.

That colt was the ugliest thing I ever saw in my life. He wasn't smooth and well proportioned like Selim. His hocks were so big they looked like satchels tied on his jay-bird legs. His little body was poor and his flanks were hollow and his legs were so long that he seemed to be standing on stilts. He had lack-lustre eyes, a gaunt head, and a long neck.

The old man came out of the barn and looked the colt over. 'Well, which one are you going to take, Son?'

'Why, Selim, of course.'

'Very well, but Brother is getting the best horse.'

'I'm not sure that ugly thing is a horse. It looks like you bred Nell to a giraffe.'

'That colt will make one of the finest saddle animals in the country.'

I didn't believe it. My brother took charge of his colt, which he named Don, but couldn't do much with him. He was wilder and more nervous than his mother. I had got Selim so he would follow me around and I trained him to shake hands and nod his head.

At six months Don was just as wild and almost as ugly as ever. When we put him in the stable or lot to separate him from his mother, he butted his head and skinned his knees on the stable door, and he jumped into a barbed-wire fence two or three times and got cut nearly all over. It was a wonder he didn't kill himself. He was so high-strung and excitable nobody could do anything with him.

Charley said, 'I doubt if anybody will ever even ride that horse, much less work him.'

The old man had been intending to break Nell to the buggy for a long time, but some reason or other had put it off. But one day he decided to get it over with. She was still pretty wild and had to be watched all the time. Only the day before, Charley dropped the lines while she was hitched to the wagon and she had run away, dragging Star along with her. The team ran from the manure pile to the back of the barn where the fence was.

Well, the old man got Nell hitched up and got into the buggy. Nell had a very long, strong tail, and when the old man gathered up the lines she threw her tail over one of them. This frightened her and pulled her head over to one side. She jerked out of Charley's hand — he'd been holding her head — and cut the front wheels of the buggy sharp, and back so much she tilted it on two wheels. Then she lunged forward and sideways so fast that over the buggy went. As it upset, with the old man caught under it, Nell changed her tactics and started running. I thought the old man would be killed. He was dragged a little way under the buggy; then it dropped him. We ran over to see how bad he was hurt. Nell was running toward the lot as hard as she could go.

The old man was getting to his feet when we reached him. 'Stop that mare!' he yelled. Nell stopped when she got to the lot gate and stood there trembling.

The old man started after us, but soon stopped with his hand on his abdomen. 'Help me to the house,' he said. 'That mare' — his breath coming in great gasps — 'don't take her out. It will ruin her.'

My mother called the doctor after we had got the old man to bed. It was lucky that our rural telephone was working that day, because he seemed to be hurt pretty bad.

The doctor finally came and went into the room and shut the door. The old man didn't want any of us to see him examined. He never would let any of us see him naked. When he took a bath he bathed the upper part of his body first and then dressed before he bathed the other half. He never let cold interfere with his bath. Sometimes he had to break the ice in the pitcher, but that didn't bother him. The colder the water the better.

After a while the doctor came out. My mother asked, 'Is it serious?' and the doctor said, 'He'll be all right in a few days. But after all, he is getting up in years and though he's got a wonderful constitution, he'll just have to take care of himself. Try and get him to quit breaking in wild horses.'

The doctor had told the old man not to get out of bed for two weeks. But he was up in a few days, working as hard as ever.

The second year the crops looked fine. The land was already showing a little improvement. The young fields of carefully weeded corn looked neat as a pin. The old man had turned under considerable cowpeas the fall before, and no doubt that had some effect. He turned under all the green and dry vegetation that he could get hold of. Other farmers burned their corn stalks and even the dead grass, but not the old man.

That summer we lost the services of Uncle Cleany. ''Pears like I ain't been pert lately,' he said. Old man Cleany (to this good day I don't remember his name) was getting pretty feeble.

The old man said, 'Well I guess you're too old to work. Maybe you'd better take out. Didn't you say you had a sister over across Brushy Mountain?'

'That's right, Brother Mac.'

'There's one thing I want to ask you, Cleany,' said the old man. 'Why is it you won't ever take a bath? Are you afraid of the water?'

'Now, Brother Mac, baths is onhealthy. A body couldn't never stand a bath except in the hot summer. A bath at my age would kill me.'

'You old fool, it would do you good,' snapped the old man. 'I take a cold bath every morning.'

'When a body ain't used to it, he can't stand it, though. Did I ever tell you about what happened to my cousin, Affro Brigant? He taken down with the measles and went into a heavy rainstorm and the next day he was dead. Cousin Affro always told me to keep away from water. He never taken a bath, but look what water did for him.'

The old man paid Uncle Cleany off and we never saw him again, but we heard he died soon after. Uncle Josh Choate, who stopped by and talked to the old man, told us about it.

'You know, there's something strange about the way Cleany died,' he said.

'What's that?' said the old man impatiently. He was always irritated by Uncle Josh's way of talking.

'Yes, mighty strange. Taken down sick with pneumony. Was caught in a heavy shower and died a few days after that.'

'Funny,' mused the old man, 'his dying that way, the way he hated water. If he'd taken a bath occasionally, it wouldn't have been such a shock to his system.

'I sure need another hand, Uncle Josh,' said the old man. 'There's more work than Charley and I can do. You don't know where I could get one, do you?'

'How about Dee Daggles?' asked Uncle Josh.

'He's busy helping chop cotton. I've got to get some-body pretty soon so my crop won't be lost. The weeds are beginning to get ahead of us, and the way it's been raining, we'll never be out of the grass.'

'Well, if I hear of a hand, I'll send him around.'

In the late summer, after the corn had come in, it took us a long time to feed. We had to go out into the field and cut the stalks of green corn and take an axe and cut them up, so the stock would eat them. The old man always planted half an acre of early corn in the garden for the table and for the stock. After we got the horses and cattle fed, we had to milk and draw water.

One afternoon a big strapping fellow came up and asked for the old man. 'Well what can I do for you?' he asked.

'I wanted to see about work. I heered you had work for a man,' the young fellow said.

'Well, yes, I might be able to use you. I might give you a day or so's work. I'll give you a dollar a day.'

'All right,' said the young fellow, and left.

The next morning a slim gangling fellow showed up about eight o'clock.

'What do you want?' asked the old man, who was pick-ing up cobs in the horse lot.

'My brother said you needed a hand. He saw you last night.'

'I thought he wanted to work.'

'No, reckon not. He wanted a job for me.'

'What's your name?'

'Reckon they call me Will.'

'Will what?' asked the old man.

'Will Thornton.'

'Well, Will, you can start to work. Get a hoe and file out of the shed there and start cutting pea vines. Angus, you show him.'

Will shuffled into the shed and shuffled out with a hoe. He moved like he had a fifty-pound weight in each shoe.

''Low it might rain,' he said, as he walked down to the field. I set him to cutting pea vines where Charley was already working.

Will was the slowest hand I ever saw. He dragged around like he was half-dead. But the old man kept him on because he worked such long hours.

We had a big dining-room, and when we had company the hands ate at the same table. One day some visiting preachers were having dinner with us and poor old Will, who wasn't used to city folks, looked as though he wanted to go through a knothole.

During the meal the old man got exasperated by Will's table manners. We had a butter knife but Will paid no attention to it. He always ate with his knife, and would shovel off a quarter of a pound of butter with it after it had been in his mouth. That hand could eat more butter than anybody I ever saw. This time he reached over to take about half the butter as usual. The old man grabbed Will's knife and laid it back on his plate; then he snatched up the butter knife and said, 'Will, use this,' and he handed it to him.

Will was so surprised and embarrassed that he dropped the knife on the plate and didn't take any butter. We ate on for a few minutes, nobody saying anything, and Will red as a beet.

Then he turned in his chair away from the window and craned his neck around the back of it, until by straining he could see out of the window.

'Looks like it might rain,' he said. But he had strained so much that he lost his balance and fell out of his chair and rolled on the floor.

We had been tickled at Will before, but now we couldn't hold ourselves. This threw the whole bunch into stitches. We laughed and laughed. Poor Will shuffled out of the room.

He wasn't a bad hand, though, after the old man trained him how to work. What he liked about Will was that he never watched the clock. He'd work from daylight to dark without complaining. And he'd keep on in the rain too; that is, until the old man took out.

That year it seemed to us that it rained every day. The crops were good, except that they were a little foul. The old man had sowed oats in the west field where the gully was, and he got a good crop considering how thin the land was. Of course, he had turned under a crop of cowpeas the year before, which enriched it some, but the soil was still thin.

Finally in late June, the sky cleared after it had been raining almost every day for six weeks. The oats were rank and green, but after a few days of hot sunshine the grain was in the milk and the old man decided to cut it.

'You ought to wait until the oats are in the dough, Brother Mac,' said Charley.

'I'm anxious to get that field cut, cured, and in the barn before it rains again. This seems to be a wet season. You know in Oklahoma one extreme follows another.'

'That's right, Brother Mac. You know one time a man was plowing in Oklahoma and it got so hot one of his horses fell down from the heat. But do you know, Brother Mac, before he could get the poor animal out of the traces there came a blizzard and it froze to death.'

'Yes, I've heard that story before. Only I thought it was Texas. Well, boys, it's burning daylight. Let's get out to the field.'

The old man set about getting ready to cradle the oats. He could have used a mower but there wasn't any this side of Dave Scott's, which was six miles away, and he figured he could save time by using the cradle. He liked it anyway. He had bought two of them when we first moved out.

'My daddy,' he said, 'was a little man, but one of the best cradlers in Mississippi. I'm not bad myself. Well, Charley, you take one of them and I'll take the other. We'll start on opposite sides of the field.'

'Cradling is shore heavy work, Brother Mac,' said Charley.

The old man laughed. He knew how to get Charley. It never failed. 'Maybe you're too light for it. Maybe I should get some hand that's stouter to do the heavy work. You could help around the house,' he said.

Charley roared, 'I never did see a man that could work me down! Didn't I sling a sledgehammer with you all winter? Didn't Dee Daggles and Uncle Cagey and Uncle Cleany have to take out because they couldn't stand it?'

'Oh, you are a fair hand for light jobs, Charley,' said the old man, trying to keep a straight face.

Charley snorted and stomped off toward the oat field,

a whet rock in one hand and the cradle over his shoulder.

The old man and Charley cut that field of oats in record time. Charley wouldn't stop to rest at all. I think he was trying to work the old man down, but he was sure foolish to try that. No one in the country was as strong as the old man.

Finally the field was all cut, and after a day or two of sunshine, the old man and Charley went out and tied the oats in hands and then bundles. They shocked the bundles in windrows across the field. The oats were still a little green, but the old man was anxious to get them shocked up before it began raining again. The skies were overcast and the air was heavy and sultry, so that it looked threatening most of the time.

Sure enough one Sunday morning, the day after the oats were tied and shocked up, it started sprinkling a little. The old man was out in the lot hooking up the team when I came down to feed about six or six-thirty.

'What are you hooking up the team for?' I asked.

'Never mind the questions. Don't you see the oats are going to be ruined? Go to the house. Get your mother. Get your sister, get your brother. And if you see any neighbor passing along tell him to come and help us. Hurry, hurry, hurry. We're going to lose our oats.'

'But it's Sunday,' I protested. 'Are you going to work on Sunday?'

'Can't you see, boy, the ox is in the ditch!' yelled the old man. 'We'll have to hump it if we're to save those oats.'

I got the family out and we all pitched in loading the oats onto the wagon. Charley, of course, was not there.

He lived at the foot of Badger and since it was Sunday he had gone home.

The old man used the pitchfork to toss the oats up on the wagon to me. After we got the bed full and tramped down, I laid the bundles so that they would extend over the edge. Each layer laid longways of the wagon pinned the ends of the first layer down.

The oats were so green that they were easy to handle and didn't slide off. That was the reason the old man was so anxious to get them into the barn. He knew that if one of those long Oklahoma rainy spells ever got started the oats would be blackened on the outside of the shock, while on the inside they would mold and rot.

When we got them stacked up a few feet above the bed the old man crawled up on top. 'Now,' he said, 'you and your mother and sister hand me oats.'

We kept handing bundles up to him until finally the load grew so high that we had to hand them up on the end of a pitchfork. He stacked the hay higher and higher.

'Don't you think that is enough?' asked my mother, who wasn't used to this kind of work.

'No, we haven't got a load on yet,' replied the old man. 'I'm afraid it is going to rain.'

The sky in the meantime had become more overcast. The clouds grew bigger and closer and blacker, and to the west lean streaks of lightning flashed across the sky.

We kept stacking the oats higher and higher until the old man stood ten or twelve feet above us. The great load approached a point at the top. It didn't look as though any more bundles would stay in place but still he kept calling for them.

Finally, just as the first few big drops of rain fell, he said, 'Just a few more bundles and we will go. I certainly hate to lose these fine oats.'

And we kept on. The rain increased until in a minute there was a hard downpour, while the lightning flashed in long angry streaks clear across the darkened sky.

'That will be enough!' yelled the old man. 'Hand me the lines.' And I took the knotted lines from my brother who had been holding the horses all this time and hooked them over a prong of the pitchfork and handed them up to him.

The team was growing excited because of the coming rain. When the thunder rumbled and there were terrific claps, they pranced and chomped their bits. The old man clucked to them and they started to the house, the rest of the family following the wagon in the now heavy storm.

Often when it rains in Oklahoma, there is a strong wind which seems to bring the water in almost solid waves. The heaviness of the rain together with the darkened sky makes it impossible to see more than a few feet in front of you.

We pulled our hats down over our eyes to shield them from the gusts of water and quickened our pace. The team was almost in a trot. I was just behind the wagon when between the rumbling of the thunder, the clanking of the wheels, and the sound of the driving rain, I heard the wagon strike some rocks and jerk the tongue first one way and then the other. Now, you know that loose hay piled high is very easily upset. If it is jarred, the whole load may slide off. The wheels had run into one of the old man's rock dams. He had not seen it on account of the rainstorm.

I looked at the high load of hay with the old man poised on top. Usually we tied a rope from the front of the wagon over the hay to the back gate, but to-day we had not had time.

The great load trembled and slipped a little. The old man evidently felt it going and shifted his weight to hold it down. The whole gigantic mass tilted over to one side and then quickly slid off the wagon, carrying the old man with it. He was carried twenty feet through the air in a semicircle and deposited on the ground all mixed up with the hay. On the way down, the lines had been jerked from his hands.

The team, nervous because of the storm and suddenly relieved of a major part of the load they were pulling, broke into a gallop, and when they realized that there was no one holding them back, they went even faster. In a few seconds they were in a dead run headed for the house, jumping gullies and rock dams and jerking the wagon this way and that.

We helped the sputtering old man out of the hay. He was not hurt, only wet and angry. He pushed us aside roughly. 'Stop that team. Those mares will be ruined,' and he started running toward the house after the wagon, which was almost out of sight.

The rest of us trailed along behind, bedraggled and unhappy. We knew that the crop was ruined and that all our labor of the morning was lost. Even the oats we had loaded onto the wagon would be spoiled.

The team ran as hard as they could up to the lot fence

and were standing there chomping their bits when we caught up with them. The old man took them out, fuming all the time. 'The oats are ruined. They will rot in the field, and those mares are ruined too. They'll run away now every chance they'll get.'

10

IT'S THE ABOMINABLE COMMERCIAL SYSTEM THAT MAKES PEOPLE SO MEAN

IN THE days that followed we watched the daily showers and the sunless days mold and ruin the oat crop. A little of it we carried to the barn, but it even molded there, the air was so damp. The sun hid its face for weeks and the showers tapered off into one drizzle after another.

The green crops grew very fast, the corn especially. This was a plant that was most affected by drouth, and consequently when it rained it shot up toward the sky, some of the stalks growing to a height of ten or twelve feet. 'Looks like bottom corn,' the old man said.

But the grass and weeds, the enemy of row crops, grew fast too, and the ground was so wet it couldn't be plowed. Our sandy hill was the driest land for miles around, but even it, except for a few spots, was too wet.

We plowed the upper side of the corn field, but the horses bogged down on the lower side.

The crab grass grew so fast it soon got out of bounds and began to choke the corn. Weeds appeared everywhere and the Bermuda that we thought was dead from the drouth of the year before came to life. It sent out runners eight or ten feet long and it fastened its roots into the ground so tightly that it was very difficult to remove.

The Bermuda attacked my mother's flower garden, and the long tentacles of grass wound themselves around the roses, the geraniums, the hollyhocks, the sweet peas, and even the flags, and threatened to choke them to death. The old man had buried a one-by-six about two inches in the ground and run it all the way around the flower garden to keep the Bermuda out, but the grass went under and over the board and attacked the flowers.

Grass and weeds grew everywhere in the fence corners, in the yard, in the pastures, and in the growing crops of cowpeas, cane, corn, peanuts, and vegetables. The old man waged continuous war to save the garden and the crops.

With our hands we removed the Bermuda runners from the flowers. We pulled up the roots and threw them out. We pulled weeds and grass out of the garden from among the strawberries and the vegetables. We threw great quantities of luscious lamb's-quarter and careless weeds and pursley to the young shotes, who ate them greedily.

'Hogs like pursley just as much as you boys like pumpkin pie,' said the old man.

There was no worry about water now. The wells were almost full and there was water standing in the flat places in the pastures and the lower part of the field. A lot of the corn on the lower side turned yellow from too much rain. Water stood on it so much that it was drowned out, and the oats on the north side blackened and molded and rotted. Cutworms attacked the corn and a lot of the roasting-ears were blackened and discolored from some kind of fungus growth. The tomatoes in the garden rotted on the ground. There wasn't enough sun to ripen them and the plants mostly went to the weed. They grew so big and bushy and heavy that they fell down on the ground, breaking the trunk. The old man tied some of them with string to strong stakes in the ground. Other vegetables rotted to some extent, including the straw-berries (many of which never ripened), and the little green cantaloupes and the muskmelons and the watermelons where they were lying in water.

We fought the grass and the weeds, though, and many of the crops did well. The corn in the garden produced two big ears to the stalk, and the Kentucky wonder beans that the old man had planted by the corn hung in great numbers on the tall stalks. The corn on the upper side of the field did well also, and the little peach trees in the orchard grew very fast.

But it was the Bermuda that made the most headway. In the chicken yard it covered the ground with a solid mat, in spite of the fact that the fifty Rhode Island Reds which my mother had raised that year kept picking at it.

'Now is the time to set the Bermuda pasture back of the orchard. It will get a good start in a wet season like this,' said the old man.

There were a few days of dry weather, and it was at this time that the old man got Dee Daggles to work for us. Dave Daggles, Dee's father, was bad after whiskey, but he didn't let Dee know it if he could help it. Dee and Dave used to steal each other's whiskey and hide it.

One day that summer when Dee was working for us, one of the Argile boys came by and called him over to the fence. Dee went over and talked to him a long time and then went down in the field where the old man was.

'Mr. McDonald, could you advance me seventy-five cents on my wages?' he asked.

'Well, Dee, I guess I could. What do you want it for?' asked the old man.

'I need it right bad,' said Dee. 'Sometimes a man needs a little cash money right bad.'

'Well, Dee, I don't have any money in my pocket,' said the old man.

'I need seventy-five cents right bad,' said Dee.

'I could write a check, I guess.'

'I need seventy-five cents cash money. Cash money was what I wanted,' said Dee.

'Well, Dee, I'll see if we can't scare up seventy-five cents for you. Go up to the house, Angus, and see if your mother's got seventy-five cents.'

When I got back with the money, Dee said, 'Mr. McDonald, I shore appreciate this. I shore do.'

Dee went over to the fence and the Argile boys came out of the thicket. They talked to Dee a few minutes and left.

Dee worked along a little while and then went over to the thicket and pulled out a bottle and took a big swig. During the morning he went over there half a dozen times. His work got slower and slower.

About eleven-thirty the old man came over to where he was. 'What's the matter, Dee?'

'Well, nothing,' said Dee. 'Nothing at all.'

Dee chopped at a careless weed with his hoe, missed it, and cut down a stalk of corn. The old man watched him narrowly. He cut down another stalk of corn and left another weed. The old man wanted his corn thinned, but not that way. He always had it thinned until there was a stalk about every three and a half feet. 'Bottom land,' he said, 'can grow good corn much thicker, but on upland you have to have a thin stand to make good corn.'

'Dee,' he said, 'what was it you wanted with that seventy-five cents?'

'I just wanted some cash money.'

'What did you want it for?'

'I needed some cough syrup.'

'What is that bottle in your pocket?'

'That's just cough syrup.'

'Let me see it.'

The old man reached over and took the bottle out of Dee's pocket, uncorked it, smelled it, and poured it out on the ground. It was characteristic of him that he didn't break the bottle. He always saved everything. Every nail, every broken strap or tool was always put away. We had a box for old nails, another of bolts, screws and so forth. We even saved all the cobs and chips to use for kindling.

The old man didn't say anything for a minute, and neither did Dee. 'Well, Dee, you can go now and come back when you sober up. I want no drunken fool on my place.' The old man put the empty bottle in his pocket after he was sure all the whiskey was out of it.

Uncle Dave came over that afternoon. 'Now, Brother Mac, I'm right sorry at that trick Dee pulled. I'm right sorry.'

'The fellow that sold him the whiskey was more to blame,' said the old man.

'Them Argiles,' said Uncle Dave, 'air ruining my boys. These whiskey peddlers ought to be run out of the country. It's pretty bad. But hit's a good joke on you, Brother Mac. That's the first time I ever heard of a preacher furnishing money to buy whiskey with.'

It was characteristic of the old man that he didn't blame Dee for drinking. Although he was intolerant of sin and was harsh in condemning people to their faces, afterward, when speaking of drunkenness or even stealing, he would say, 'It's the system; it's the abominable commercial system that makes people so mean.'

I don't know how he figured the banks were responsible for drinking, but he seemed to connect the two.

About the only thing he didn't excuse was laziness in a man and immodesty in a woman. These, I guess, were the two cardinal sins on his list. He'd excuse murder and drunkenness a lot quicker.

There were quite a few murderers in our community. I know of one Indian who had killed several men and his first wife. He had a mania for killing his wife when he got drunk. I remember one time when he got drunk and took his gun and started looking for her, but she had hidden herself. He couldn't find any of his friends or relatives to kill, so he went out and killed a man he didn't know.

This Indian was one of the old man's best friends. This seems strange, but the old man was lenient on murder when the murderer was a good provider. And the Indian was as model a husband and father as you could find anywhere when he was sober. 'Too bad about Sam Big Cloud,' the old man said. 'Why, he is as good a worker as you'll find in the whole Cherokee Nation. You'll always find meat in that Indian's smokehouse, and he always keeps his fences up and his wife in wood and water.'

There was a good deal of feeling against Big Cloud, though, about this last killing. Ordinarily a killing didn't attract much attention, there being so many of them, but it seems in this case the dead man had a wife and eight children to support. To make it worse, Big Cloud hadn't known the man he had killed at all. He was a complete stranger and he had shot him in cold blood.

Big Cloud sent word after the killing that he wouldn't let anybody take him. That put the authorities in a tough spot. They knew old man Big Cloud was one of the best shots in the country and that he'd probably kill a dozen men before he could be captured. It was especially embarrassing because the Indian's son was town marshal.

Big Cloud was still drunk and had barricaded himself in his room. It seems that he had got over his desire to kill his wife. So Big Cloud's son sent his mother in to talk to him.

'You tell Boy to come get me,' Big Cloud is reported to have said. 'Nobody else come.' What he meant was that he would surrender to his son, but not to anyone else.

Some of the local people thought that was right sweet. 'Big Cloud really has a heart of gold,' they said. 'When he's sober, he's gentle as a lamb.' And the old man shook his head and said, 'And he's such a good provider, too. What a pity!'

There was a preliminary court trial and the old man was called in to testify to the Indian's good character.

Big Cloud never did go to the pen. This was a little unusual. Ordinarily, in Sallisaw, a man went to the pen for a couple of years when he murdered somebody. The lawyers got Big Cloud's bottom farm, though, or so they said.

The old man reminded Uncle Dave about this incident when they were talking about Dee's drinking. 'Dave, you ought to set a good example to your boys and not drink yourself. You don't want anything to happen to them like what happened to Sam Big Cloud.'

'Oh, Brother Mac,' replied Dave, 'I never tech the stuff.' And then a little uneasily, trying to change the subject, he said, 'How about borrowing your planter?'

The land Dave cultivated had all sorts of snags and stumps on it. The old man had suggested to him that he clean up his place, clear off the timber, and dig out the roots and stumps, but he paid no attention. There were a lot of rocks on his place, too, but Uncle Dave had never picked up a one.

'Dave,' said the old man, 'I'm afraid your rough land would tear my planter all to pieces. It's a new one and I wouldn't like to have it broken. I guess I'll have to turn you down.'

'Well, Brother Mac, now that ain't neighborly.'

'I'm sorry, Dave, but you see if I don't take care of my stuff no one else will.'

Uncle Dave was good-natured, though. 'I guess maybe I can borrow old man Cassidy's.' He took out his box of Scotch snuff and took a big dip.

'The only thing I like about that snuff is its name,' said the old man.

'It's shore good snuff.'

'Well, come back, Dave, when you want to borrow something else. I'll lend it to you if I can. How is Muley these days?'

'Seems like Muley's always complaining,' said Uncle Dave. 'She eats good, though.'

'Aunt Muley looks like she's got pellagra. Have you ever had the doctor come out and look at her? Dave, if you'd raise a garden, you'd get along a lot better. Why don't you?'

'Landlord won't let me have no ground.'

'You mean the landlord won't let you have a garden spot?'

'He said that on any of the good land I have to raise cotton or else pay him five dollars for a garden spot. I ain't got the five. Seems like everybody is against the poor man. Between the banker and the landlord, I guess I'll never have nothin'. Muley gets more poorly all the time. Looks like the woman is going to die. What she needs is green stuff, but about all the green stuff she gits is poke salit.'

'Dave, you go on up to the house and we'll fix up a poke for you. I think we've got some vegetables that are going to spoil if they're not eaten.'

'Well, now, Brother Mac, that's real neighborly of you. Muley will like that a heap. Brother Mac, do you reckon you could spare me a little bait of fatback? We ain't had no meat for a month.'

'Isn't the bank carrying you this year?' asked the old man.

'Yes, they're carrying me all right, but I couldn't get but fifty dollars, and they wouldn't let me have but a few dollars till cotton-chopping time, and we've et that up.'

'Dave, you oughtn't to go in debt. You ought to try and make one crop without borrowing money. Then you'd be all right.'

'No use, Brother Mac. The rich has got us pore folks, lock, stock, and barrel. We pore people sure ain't got no chanct. I signed a note for seventy-five dollars, but I only git fifty dollars — ten dollars at a time in crop time. I ask you, Brother Mac, is that right? The pore man hasn't got no chanct.'

The old man didn't reply to Uncle Dave's argument. He changed the subject, which was his habit when he didn't want to answer a question. He talked about some new ground Dave was putting in.

Uncle Dave had tried to put in some land that year so he would have something left over when he paid off his note at the bank. There were ten acres just north of our place that never had been cleared, and it wasn't all washed to pieces like most of the land he farmed.

'You ought to cut that timber and make posts out of the post oaks and black locusts,' said the old man. 'When I was sixteen years old I split three hundred and twenty rails in one day. I always was a good hand in the timber.

A good farmer keeps his fences up so the stock won't break in.'

He had advised Dave many times about his farming, but Uncle Dave never paid any attention. He never had more than a few days' supply of firewood ahead, and his fences were half-down.

Uncle Dave had an old broken-down, swaybacked, spavined team. One of the horses was so thin you could hang your coat on his hip bones. I never saw such a poor horse. The old man said you had to stand him up twice to make a shadow.

The next day my brother and I were walking to the hill on the way to one of the neighbors to borrow a clevis. Old Uncle Dave came driving along with a little jag of wood he was taking to town to sell.

'Git on, boys,' said Uncle Dave, 'git on and ride. Giddap, Heavy,' he said after we'd climbed onto the wagon.

'What do you call your lead horse "Heavy" for?' asked my brother. 'He looks light to me.'

'He may look light, but you'd think he was heavy if you had to lift him up every morning. You'd think he was real heavy, you shore would.'

The dry spell didn't last long. Soon it started raining again, and this time the weather didn't fool around. God really opened the heavens. A general rain descended on eastern Oklahoma. For the first time the old man missed his appointment at Dwight. Big Sallisaw was half a mile wide in some places. It rained a steady downpour for a week and all the first bottoms were flooded. There were reports that the Arkansas, the Illinois, the Neosho, and all the creeks were out of bounds. Many people were caught in the flood and barely escaped with their lives. Joe Alexander, the millionaire potato king, lost thousands of bushels of potatoes.

The Greenwood Junction farm was completely flooded. The old man took the train to Fort Smith to see how bad the flood was. When he returned I met him at the station. I drove Star down to Sallisaw to bring him out so he wouldn't have to walk home. On the way he told me how the railroad clerk at Fort Smith had given him too much money when he had bought his ticket.

'Did you give it back?' I asked.

'No, I didn't notice it until I got on the train. I'll tell you, I don't think I will. The thievish railroads are responsible for a great deal of poverty in our country. I tell you, son, the railroads and corporations have almost ruined this country.'

'Well,' I said, 'it seems strange, though, that you would take the railroad's money when you wouldn't take a cent from anyone else that wasn't yours. You say the banks are thievish too, but you always pay back every penny you borrow.'

'I never said your Uncle Henry's bank was thievish. There never was a more honest boy than Henry.'

'Well, other banks,' I persisted.

The old man seemed to be in one of his more tolerant moods and I was arguing with him, something I didn't often do.

'Listen, son. You have got to understand a few fundamentals. You know that I am always honest and all the

McDonalds are always honest in their dealings with people. I advocate being honest, even with crooks. You can't have any kind of society unless people pay their debts. When I sign a note at the bank I promise to pay, and if I didn't and if nobody else did, then the whole structure of society would fall apart. There would be anarchy and every man would have to be his own policeman and nobody's property and home would be safe. When I condemn the banks, the railroads, and the corporations, I don't mean everybody else should go to stealing too.

'But if the majority of the people decide, if the plain people decide in a body that they will take back what the railroads have stolen from them, it would be all right. That would be in line with Woodrow Wilson's and William Jennings Bryan's principles.'

I shook my head in confusion. 'I don't understand it,' I said. 'I didn't know that William Jennings Bryan and Woodrow Wilson advocated any such thing.'

'Well, you are a little young to understand, but I will try to explain a little history to you,' said the old man. 'I learned all this in the way Lincoln did. I used to read history books by the light of my daddy's fireplace after splitting rails all day.

'You know I was one of the best rail-splitters in the community. When I was eighteen years old I could split three hundred and twenty rails in a day.'

'You were going to tell me some history.' I had heard about the rail-splitting many times.

'Oh, yes. Well, in the beginning a poor man had a chance to go out and lay claim to a farm and build a home and improve his land and raise his family in the nurture and admonition of the Lord. There was land for everybody because our Revolutionary forefathers had won the war against the English Tories, and men like Jefferson and Tom Paine had kept scoundrels like Alexander Hamilton from making an autocracy out of the government we had fought for and under which the plain people enjoyed real democracy. But Hamilton was such a clever schemer that he got Washington and a lot of other patriotic people to agree to a national bank system and other things, which have been a burden to the poor people ever since. The result was that the commercial class that Jefferson fought against so hard has been riding on the backs of the poor farmers ever since.

'The banks, the corporations, and the commercial class are responsible for much of the poverty you see today. Andrew Jackson, who in some ways was a greater man than Jefferson, fought against the banks, but when he died the financial interest came back stronger than ever.

'And after the Civil War, the railroads stole the west from the people. The people paid for the railroads many times over.'

'How was that?' I asked. 'How could the people pay when they were so poor?'

'How can you be so dull, my boy? Don't you learn anything in your history books? Don't you know about how the Republican Party opened up the Treasury of the United States and turned over millions of acres of land to the railroads after the Civil War? Now, I believe that the Government should tax the corporations and get back a little of what they have stolen from the people. I be-

lieve, and Woodrow Wilson and William Jennings Bryan
believe, that the money interests and Wall Street are part
of a vicious system which is strangling our democratic
institutions.'

The old man was really getting warmed up to his subject. He was already at the point where he resented my
asking a question.

I ventured to ask about the Arkansas River flood, but
he didn't even hear me.

'Yes,' he went on, 'the Republican Party stole the
country from the poor people. The commercial class has
got the farmers lock, stock, and barrel. William Jennings
Bryan tried to get the Government away from the financial interests, but he failed. Now, Woodrow Wilson, I
believe, has got a fighting chance. Under the Federal
Reserve System, the banking system will be returned to
the people. There's a lot more will have to be done,
though.'

'How about the flood?' I asked for the third time.
I was interested in the old man's political tirades, but I
had heard most of what he was saying before, particularly
what he said about Woodrow Wilson.

'Oh, yes, the flood. Oh, it's pretty bad. Most of our
land is under water. There is water all over Moffet.
People are rowing around their houses in boats.'

Crops were destroyed and much livestock was drowned.
Our little hill place did not escape the general destruction.
The big intense rain came the day after the old man had
walked across the railroad trestle to make his appointment
at Dwight. The creek was so high and so swift that a
horse couldn't swim it. All day and all night there was a

solid downpour. The rain came down in sheets. There was water everywhere. One of the chicken coops was floated clear away and a lot of the little chicks were caught in the storm and drowned. There were dead chickens stretched everywhere.

We spent most of the day trying to bring them back to life. Of course a lot of them were too far gone to revive.

'I'd like to go down and see how the dams are standing this flood,' said the old man. 'I have never seen a rain like this. It will probably play the wild with some of the little dams. The big ones will hold, though, I think.'

The next morning the rain ceased abruptly and the sun came out once again. The drops of water that hung everywhere on the vegetation glistened in the bright sunshine. The old man headed for the west field. He was anxious to see if his dams were washed out. I caught up with him when he stopped at the brow of the hill, his favorite point of vantage when he wanted to get a bird's-eye view.

He stood and looked at the hillside and shook his head. 'Look at my dams.'

There had been twenty-five dams in the long, deep gully. We had worked many days to build them and hauled hundreds of loads of rocks. Now most of the rocks were washed out and scattered in harum-scarum fashion down the slope. In some places the water had washed out the center of the dam and left the ends, and in others it had washed out one end and left the other. Sometimes the dam had just merely crumpled; the walls had evidently collapsed because the water had completely undermined them. Rocks were scattered in great disorder and for a great distance. It looked as though someone had removed them one by one and tossed them at random down the bottom of the gully. The dams nearest us at the top of the slope were fairly intact. The downrushing water had merely gone around them, forming an entirely new channel and leaving them high and dry.

The old man walked back and forth mumbling and muttering to himself. He did not roar and stomp his feet, as he often did when he was angry. He just stood and gazed at the field and the deepened gully and the rocks and said nothing.

I felt vaguely uneasy to see the old man like this. It seemed that no matter how hard he worked there was always something to spoil what he had done.

The old man stood and looked at the devastation, and for the first time I thought he looked a little beaten. He looked almost sad as he stood there. Then he gritted his teeth, stomped his foot, and shook his fist. He didn't say anything but I could tell he was in a rage. Then I felt better. He was his old self again.

11

THE FOUNDATION OF CIVILIZATION IS
BEING UNDERMINED

ALTHOUGH we had already laid by our corn when the flood came, the old man insisted that Charley run the middles with two big buzzard sweeps on a double-shovel stock. The old man went ahead of the plow and broadcast cowpeas. The sweeps just barely scratched the ground so they wouldn't disturb the corn roots.

Then he set about rebuilding the dams, and it was not long before the field looked as neat as ever. The big gully wasn't washed out as badly as it had first appeared. It had filled up a great deal before the flood came. The water had not washed it out as deep as it had been when the old man first bought the place. No doubt the dams and rocks and other obstructions had slowed down the water so that it dropped some of the mud it was carrying.

The rain had stopped for good. As is usual in Oklahoma, the flood was followed by a long dry spell. This was good because it gave the cotton bolls a chance to mature; that is, those that the boll-weevils hadn't ruined. In a wet season, especially one preceded by a light winter, the boll-weevils were usually pretty bad.

That year all the crops that weren't drowned out were rank. The cotton was high as your head in the bottoms and many of the ears of corn were so high you could scarcely reach them.

Cotton is a dry-weather crop. It doesn't need much rain, particularly in the latter part of the season, and so the drouth which causes corn farmers so much grief is a blessing to the lowland cotton farmers.

This year the cotton in the bottom went to weed and the boll-weevil had a picnic. The great enemy of a good cotton crop, it was making its way slowly north about this time from Texas, and every year in the wet-land areas was destroying millions of bolls of cotton. It buried itself in the young bolls, and ate and grew fat and kept them from ever opening.

The cotton farmers learned to dread a wet August, for that is the critical period in the life of a boll. The hot August sun was needed for the fully developed cotton plants, to retard its green branchy leafy growth and mature the bolls.

In September, if the boll weevils hadn't destroyed them

and if there had been enough sun, the bolls would slowly open and the cotton fiber appear. When they were fully open, the women, the children, and the old men would descend upon the snowy field of cotton with long sacks thrown over their shoulders. Up one row and down another they would go until the white of the field was gone. They emptied the cotton at one end of the field, where the farmer carefully weighed it.

The field had to be picked over several times. As fast as one growth had ripened, another was slowly opening. Cotton picking in our section of Oklahoma lasted all fall and sometimes into the winter.

As the weather became colder, the fingers of the pickers got raw and sore. On the frosty mornings the sharp points of the empty bolls stuck into them and made them bleed. And the backs of the pickers became weary, but they could not stop because the farmers had to get the cotton to the gin as soon as possible.

The cotton crop had been mortgaged. The banker or the grocer had advanced money or supplies on it, and the farmers had to get it in so they could spend what remained after the debts were paid. When the price was good the season and the boll-weevils were bad, and when the crop was good the price was so low that the farmers had little or nothing left over.

But cotton picking and ginning were nevertheless activities which dominated all the life and thought of the community. It was the time when the farmer got the slim fruit of his labor.

On the Saturday after the first picking all the family would go to town. The women and children would spend their hard-earned cash for white shoes and dresses, and then tramp around in the dusty Sallisaw streets. The men and boys would get a jug of corn and congregate in the back of the stores and shoot craps, or else hide out in a more secluded place and play poker.

Occasionally some farmer would get too much to drink and go on the rampage, and the town marshal would have to throw him in jail until he sobered up.

Sometimes the poor women, who knew the weakness of their men in cotton time would follow them around, find their bottles of whiskey, and break them. Then there would be a family argument on the streets. Once in a while a man in his drunken rage would make a pass at his wife.

The wives would beg the men to come on home and behave themselves, and the men would hide or give them the slip so they could drink and gamble and cut up jack.

During these days, of course, my brother and sister and I had our noses to the grindstone, but occasionally we got an opportunity to observe the people when we went to town with the old man. He usually went in on Saturday on business, and he was constantly on the lookout for bargains in land or horses or cattle or anything else that came along. He was one of the shrewdest traders in the country.

He liked to get out and see the people on Saturday too, and chide them for not going to church on Sunday. He knew practically every man, woman, and child.

That fall Brother Pearson came to visit us. He was a Presbyterian traveling preacher who worked mostly among the Indians. He had learned several of their languages, knew Cherokee quite well, and was well known throughout Sequoyah and Adair Counties. He and the old man talked about the camp meetings they used to hold in Indian Territory.

They told about the time the old man and Brother Pearson were holding a meeting at Porum, one of the toughest spots in Oklahoma. The services were interrupted by a gun battle. There was a feud going on in the neighborhood. A lot of people were killed, and when the old man was halfway through his sermon, bullets began whistling through the church. A lot of people got down behind the benches, and others grabbed their guns and ran out and joined in the fight. The old man and Brother Pearson crouched down behind the pulpit to keep from getting hit.

Brother Pearson claimed to believe in predestination. He said that the Lord had foreordained everything, and that when a man's time came to die he would die and no one could do anything about it.

The old man laughed when he saw him trying to dodge the bullets. 'There is no use in your hiding behind the pulpit. If your time has come you will die.'

'I believe,' said Brother Pearson, 'that the good Lord foreordained that I should get behind this pulpit.'

They had a good laugh when they talked about this incident.

'What you need, Brother Mac,' said Brother Pearson, 'is a good old-fashioned revival like we used to have. I don't think the country people really get warmed up to religion until they have a good brush-arbor revival.'

'Yes,' replied the old man, 'I'm strong for the old-time

religion too. You know these country preachers are too
stiff-necked to hold revivals any more. Church members
nowadays are too nice to unbend. They're too proud.
The people in Sallisaw are too worldly to be interested in
the old-time shouting religion. Why, I remember when I
was a boy we used to hold a brush-arbor meeting every
year after the crop was laid by. Many's the time I remember my mother getting happy and shouting, "I love
everybody. Jesus is my Saviour!" '

'Why don't you hold a revival this fall, Brother Mac?'

'Next year I will. Those Badger people sure need it.
But this year I'm so far behind with my work, I haven't
got the time. We're not out of the grass yet, it has been
such a wet season, and there are more dams to build.
You see, I think one reason the west field washed so badly
was because I didn't have enough little dams to head off
the water before it reached the main gully.'

'I'll tell you what I'll do, Brother Mac. I'll help you
out with the work for a few weeks if you can manage to
hold a revival. You know, I like the farm and I've been
wanting to get out in air and do some hard work. My
muscles are getting flabby sitting around and eating your
good wife's fried chicken.'

'All right, Brother Pearson,' the old man replied.
'That's what I'll do if you help me out. I would like
nothing better than to hold a revival with you. You have
the spirit. You can touch the hearts of these wicked
people.'

In the weeks that followed, Brother Pearson worked
with us in the fields. He was the best hand I ever saw, a
big, powerful man who wasn't afraid to get his hands dirty.

He could lift as big a rock as the old man, and he knew everything there was to know about farm work.

At last we were caught up, and the old man put Charley to grubbing sprouts and went ahead with his plans for an outdoor meeting.

The men of the Badger Lee community came and helped the old man and Brother Pearson build the brush arbor. There were gasoline torches at night for light, and they borrowed some lumber for benches from the sawmill. There was singing in the morning with dinner on the ground and preaching in the afternoon and at night. The first few days there weren't any converts, but we could see that some of the people were getting warmed up.

After the service Aunt Nancy Nine-Killer, an old Indian woman, and Brother Pearson would circulate through the crowd and talk to some of the most serious-faced ones. There was one girl who had been a little worldly and she told the old man that she wanted to give her heart to God but the Devil wouldn't let her go. The old man prayed for her. She would hold up her hand when the call went out for those who wanted to be prayed for, but it didn't seem to do her much good. Some people came down to the mourners' bench, and when we had voluntary prayers they asked God to save the poor girl's soul.

Aunt Nancy Nine-Killer had been converted a long time and she prayed out every day, almost. The meeting had been going on about a week when the worldly girl put the Devil out of her soul. I remember the old man had preached a powerful sermon that night and the girl had come up to the mourners' bench and about halfway through the sermon she threw herself on the ground and just lay there crying. The old man kept on preaching, but when he prayed he asked God to get the girl out of the morass of sin. Aunt Nancy interrupted several times with 'Amen, O God, God pity, Jesus loves.' The old man went on with his prayer, telling the Lord what a struggle the girl had had. Then he called on Brother Pearson to pray. Brother Pearson walked over to where the girl was lying, kneeled down, and put his hand on her shoulder.

'Dear merciful One, look down on this poor sinner in Your Infinite Mercy and bring her safe to the fold of Jesus. O God, this girl is now in the clutches of the Devil. Help her, please, God, so that she may come home to Glory. Yes, God, we know she has sinned. We know, God, were it not for Your Infinite Mercy and Forgiveness she could never be saved. Her soul, even now, dear God, is hanging on the edge of the bottomless pit. The Devil, O God, has hold of her, pulling her down to the bottomless pits of shame and degradation. O God, banish the fleshpots from the mind of this wayward child. Help her conquer Satan. Give her courage, faith, and hope, so that she may turn over a new leaf. Wash her soul in the blood of the Lamb!'

Brother Pearson was a big red-faced man. I could see sweat popping out of his face. From all over the crowd came groans and sighs. 'Amen, God, save her. O God, save her,' was repeated over and over.

Pretty soon Brother Pearson joined in. He stopped his prayer and began saying over and over, 'Please, God, save this girl,' and the crowd began to chant, 'God save this girl.' They chimed in with the preachers and soon everybody joined in and the organist was all ready to play. The music had been going a minute or so when the girl jumped up and screamed, 'I am saved. I am saved! Praise God and Hallelujah! God be praised, I love Jesus. Jesus, You're my Saviour.' Then she grabbed Aunt Nancy Nine-Killer, threw her arms around her and kissed her, then ran about kissing and hugging those near her, telling them how much she loved Jesus and how she was saved. There was a general rejoicing. Aunt Nancy hugged the old man and kissed Brother Pearson. She ran up and down the aisle between the rows of benches. 'God be praised. Glory Hallelujah! Glory! Glory! Glory!'

God at last had touched the hearts of those people. That night the meeting lasted until eleven o'clock, and twenty-five people gave their hearts to God and thirteen united with the Church. The meeting lasted three weeks and there were over a hundred conversions.

'It was a great spiritual revival,' the old man said, 'but we'll have to work hard to make up for the times we've lost. I don't begrudge it, though.'

The old man went back to the farm and Brother Pearson told us all good-bye and went on his way.

The crops were good that year; there was plenty of hay for the stock, and the old man had so many pea vines that he had to fill the tool shed and leave the tools out in the rain. 'There's no hay like good pea hay for the milk cows,' he said. 'We can't have too much of it.' He filled the old hay barn and the cabin where the renter had lived, except for one room where he kept the smoked meat.

There is nothing better than fresh pork. We always enjoyed hog-killing time because we had fresh pork chops, ham, and liver. 'There's nothing better than hog brains fried with eggs,' the old man used to say.

The old man butchered five hogs when the first real cold
spell set in. Mr. Irwin and his oldest boy, Gross, came
up to help.

First they built up a big fire and heated water in a great
iron pot that my mother boiled clothes in. Then the boil-
ing water was poured into a barrel buried slantwise in the
ground. In front of it was a rail platform to scrape the hog
on. When everything was ready the old man got out his
twenty-two rifle to kill the fattening hogs. They had been
fed on peanuts they rooted out of the ground and corn
and cowpeas that the old man raised just for that purpose.
When they had eaten out the field feed he put them in a
pen for four weeks and fed them all the corn they could
hold.

My brother and I were sorry to see our pig, William
Jennings Bryan, killed. We had made a pet out of that
pig. He would follow us around like a dog. When we
called the hogs he was the first one to come, but he was
so lazy he never would forage very far down in the feed
field. And when the old man put him in the pen he would
rub up against the fence so that we would scratch his
back. He was such a glutton that he would gorge himself
and then lie down and grunt and groan for an hour. After
he had rested awhile he would get up on his haunches and
eat some more corn. Soon he got so fat that you could
scarcely see his eyes.

William Jennings Bryan was smart, though. When the
old man turned him into the lot so he could get a good
shot at him, he kept turning his back. Finally the old
man got a bead and fired. But as luck would have it, the
hog moved his head and the bullet went into his eye and

down through his throat. The right place to shoot a hog is right above and between the eyes so the bullet will go into the brain.

A mad hog is the hardest thing in the world to kill. William Jennings Bryan ran around the lot squealing and the old man had to shoot him four times — one bullet knocked him down, but he jumped up and ran around crazily.

Finally Charley hit him in the head with the axe, jumped astraddle of him and turned him on his back, and stabbed him in the heart with a long knife. Charley was one of the best hands at sticking a hog I ever saw. He always put his knife right through the heart. Of course every hog has to be stuck after he is shot in order to drain the blood out. William Jennings Bryan died in just a minute, giving a last squeal as he rolled over.

After the pig was killed Gross and Mr. Irwin dragged him to the barrel, which had been covered with two sacks and soused him for a minute. Then they scraped his black hair off with long sharp knives. 'I can just taste this pig now,' the old man said. But somehow my brother and I never enjoyed eating William Jennings Bryan.

After the hogs were killed and hung up the old man took a keen knife and cut them right down through the middle and took out the entrails, heart, liver, and lights.

The dressed hogs were hung up in a cold place and allowed to cool. The next day they were cut up into hams, shoulders, and middlings. My mother trimmed off the fat meat and boiled it down and made lard out of it. I guess she must have rendered two hundred pounds of lard that year. After the meat was put down in salt for a few days it was hung up in the smokehouse and smoked with hickory chips.

The fall of the year was crop-gathering time when the farmer could see the fruit of his labor. There were corn to gather, potatoes to dig, and peas to pick. The old man had us picking cowpeas for a long time. Then on the first windy day we'd thresh them. By doing that we had all the peas we wanted to eat for the winter, enough for seed, and some to sell besides. 'The farmer who doesn't raise a few cowpeas,' the old man said, 'is not any account.'

Altogether we had a good crop that year. For the first time we had enough hay for the stock, enough meat, and the shed was stacked full of wood for the winter.

When the rains came the old man watched the dams very closely. He had built a lot of little ones in the west field high up on both sides of the hill so that the water would be checked before it got to the big gully. With each rain you could see these small gullies filling up behind the dams.

The old man had had some trouble with the first dams he had built because the water ran over them like a waterfall and formed a plunge pool below, digging out the soil and undermining the dam. He had solved this problem by leaving a gap in the center for the water to go through and putting a big flat rock just below for it to fall on when it ran over the dam. When the spring rains came not a dam was destroyed by the water, though in a few places it washed around the ends.

The old man was out patching up the broken places as soon as it rained. He sowed the field in oats again. That year there was a very long drouth, but he had got the oats in early so that he had time enough to put in another crop. 'I'll make a good crop of cowpeas off that land,' he said.

We sowed them in February and got a good stand except where the rocks were too thick. The side on the east of the draw was almost level. It had been farmed a long time and the soil was almost yellow. The old man said it was an example of what sheet wash would do. But the May dry spell cut the oats short. When the old man had got them cut and raked into shocks and hauled into the barn we turned the stock in to clean up the waste grain.

That summer was almost as dry as it had been the first year, and it made the ground so hard you couldn't stick a plow into it. There was just enough clay to harden it like cement. Charley tried to argue the old man out of breaking that ground until it rained. 'Better wait until it rains. Why, you can't plow that ground.'

But the old man wouldn't pay any attention. He seemed happy that the ground had got so hard. 'We'll break it, and when it does rain it'll soak up the water and store up enough moisture. The main thing is to get your land in condition for the rain.'

We only had two small turning-plows and the breaking took some time. You couldn't cut a very wide swath because the ground was so hard. Sometimes the plow would jump out and you would have to stand it on its point to get it back in. Then the ground would break up in great lumps.

Charley cussed and said he was going to quit, but he stuck it out. 'You know,' he said to me one time, 'if the old man wasn't so stubborn he wouldn't work so hard.

He preaches the same ideas. He believes the Lord wants everybody to work all the time.' Charley was telling me that as if I hadn't heard it. That's the way the old man was, all right.

That west field got harder and harder. We had to go to the blacksmith shop two or three times to get the plow points sharpened. By this time it was July and it was plenty hot. When the plow broke up the ground into those great clods and the horses walked across the fields a huge cloud of dust followed them. My brother and I carried water to the old man and Charley.

Most of the land was broken when Charley gave out. He had been pretty quiet all day and he usually talked a blue streak. My mother said later, 'I thought he wasn't well because he only ate nine biscuits for breakfast.' Well, I took Charley some water along in the shank of the afternoon and I thought he looked a little pale. I told him so.

Charley looked angry and said, 'No old man can work me down,' and took a big swig of the water. The old man came over in the shade of the persimmon tree, took one look at Charley, and told him to go home and go to bed.

Charley started for the house, but he got sick at his stomach and vomited before he got there.

The old man went right ahead with the plowing alone. 'The soil will be in fine condition. The rain will come and the loose soil will absorb it. There won't be much run-off.'

We had to use the A-harrow to break some of the clods after the old man had finished the breaking. Sure enough, two or three days after that there came a gully-washer.

It started in raining hard one afternoon about two o'clock. Some people came to get married and we couldn't find the old man anywhere. My mother said, 'The last time I saw him he was headed toward the west field. Put on a coat and your overshoes and go and find him if you can.'

The rain was coming down in sheets and the water was running everywhere. I noticed on the way to the field that one of the ditches the old man had dug was nearly full. Well, I looked and looked and I couldn't see him, so I decided to go back to the house because I was getting wet, when I heard somebody holler down on the lower side of the field.

The old man was standing by the fence that divided his land from Cassidy's. 'Come here, son,' he said. 'I want to show you something. Look at that water coming off of Cassidy's land.'

Cassidy's field had about the same slope as ours. It had cotton on it that year and the rows were run up and down the hill. Between each row there was a little stream of water. You could see the streams all the way up the hill when the lightning flashed. Lower down and near the fence where we were, some of them had joined together to form bigger streams. I noticed that the little streams ran around the rows, but when they had joined they cut across and washed out the whole row. Some of the stalks of cotton, though they were knee-high, were washed out completely. All these combinations of streams headed for the lower side, where there was a gully.

'Now let's follow the water,' said the old man. We were soaked, but he didn't seem to know it was raining at all. We climbed the fence and followed the biggest stream that flowed from Cassidy's land a few hundred yards, and the gully got bigger all the time. There was a slope this far, but then the land began to flatten out, and a little farther on was almost level.

The gully got shallow and the water was spreading out all over the flat place. 'Tomorrow if this keeps up there will be a layer of sand and clay all over the flat. You are seeing poor land being made poorer. Now let's go back and look at our field.'

There was a good deal of water coming through the gully which ran up the draw. But there were dams to slow it down and by the time it reached the lower side only a little trickled through the rack wall by the fence. Little or none was running off the broken ground. It seemed to soak in instead.

Well, the old man stood there several minutes staring at those fields. When he looked at ours he seemed pleased, but when he looked at the deepening little gullies in between Mr. Cassidy's stunted cotton rows he got angry.

'These improvident farmers are ruining the land. Yes, ruining it world without end. The whole country is going to rack and ruin. The foundation of civilization is being undermined. There will come a time when conservation will be popular but it will be too late. When the farmers are pauperized this nation will face ruin.'

And he went on in that vein for some time. It seemed sort of silly to see him standing out in the rain preaching a sermon, but I shouldn't have dared to say what I thought.

12

GOD INTENDED HORSES TO WORK

WITH each season the old hill was changing. With each rain the gullies were filling up a little, until now we could plow over the giant one in the north field. Each year the crops of corn and peas and hay grew greater and the cockleburs less. The fight against grass and weeds and sprouts and rocks was a continuous one, but it did not require so much effort as time passed.

The rock and air farm, as the old man called it, began to produce results. For a long time now, almost four years, he had been spending a great deal of money building it up. He had had a hard time financially, and although after the first year or two we had plenty to eat, there were times when there was no money for clothes or luxuries. 'I never had so much to eat in my life and was never harder up,' he would say.

The little orchard, which was so hard to get started, began to bring in some money. The old man had set out early Wheelers and other varieties of peach trees and he had not only the finest but the earliest fruit in the country. We sold them for two and three dollars a bushel before the market was glutted. The old man raised his peaches with a great deal of care. In the early spring, when the limbs were beginning to bend from their loads of little green peaches, he would go out and thin them carefully so they would grow to a large size and if a wind storm came, as it frequently did, he tied up the broken limbs. He pruned each tree carefully to get the maximum amount of fruit.

In the late summer, when the Elbertas and the cling peaches had come in, my mother would can jar after jar of the fruit. They were the clearest and the finest in the neighborhood.

Uncle Henry came and had dinner with us one Sunday and walked over the farm with the old man.

'Well, Jim,' he said, 'you are getting along better than I expected. This farm, though, will never be a paying proposition. Without the income from your preaching job, you never would have made it. However, I will say one thing, you are making a good farm out of a poor one. I never thought you could fill these gullies and I never thought that these washy fields would make half a crop.'

'You come back and look at this farm in four years and you'll be just as surprised. The old hill is still poor in many spots, but before I'm through I'll have every foot of ground producing something. I'll make two crops a year too. You know the American farmer doesn't half use the land he's got. He ought to put in a crop of cowpeas on most of his land to enrich it. And he ought never to go to town without carrying enough stuff to pay for what he buys. That's what I want to do next — put this farm on a paying basis.'

'Well, you'll never be able to do that, I'm afraid,' replied Uncle Henry. 'In the first place, you haven't got enough land to support a family. If it weren't for your salary, you'd be starved out.'

'You wait and see,' replied the old man, a little nettled because Uncle Henry was disputing his word. 'You didn't want me to buy this land in the first place, and you said it would never produce a good crop. You said I'd never be able to make a go of it. Oh, yes, I remember when I talked to you and Delaney. You laughed at me. In fact, everybody laughed at me and my ideas. But I've made a good start toward proving you all wrong. You and these farmers have got so used to the idea of abusing the land with cotton that you think a man can't make a living without it. I tell you, if the farmers of Oklahoma never raised another stalk of cotton, it would be the best thing that ever happened for everybody concerned, including you bankers.'

'Jim,' said Uncle Henry, 'I admit you've done a lot here. I admit you're right about a farmer having a garden, a cow and some pigs and chickens. But you can't make money out of a farm in this country without cotton. You're a fanatic on the subject. And all your preaching isn't going to change things.'

'You wait and see. I'll make a good living on this twenty acres and I'll never have to ask the bank for a dollar.'

Uncle Henry went away shaking his head. He knew it was no use to argue with the old man. He never changed his mind about anything. He was stubborn and dogmatic and he was proud of it. 'I'm like the Scotchman who made this prayer: "I thank thee, Lord, that I am always right, for if I were wrang I would be eternally wrang." All this talk about two sides to a question,' the old man snorted. 'There's two sides to everything, all right — a right side and a wrong, and I'm always on the right side and I'm going to stay that way, that's all there is to it.'

With the improvements in land on the farm came improvements in stock. We had a fine little herd of Jersey cows now. Buttercup's heifer calf was due to come fresh any day now, and the other calves were coming along nicely. One of them had already been bred to Mr. Downing's bull. Mr. Downing was the school superintendent and he owned the finest Jersey bull in the country.

The old man thought a lot of Mr. Downing because he agreed with his ideas about farming. There were several of the men around town who thought the old man was a good farmer. They didn't call him a fanatic as some people did. There was old Doc Adams, who was the best authority on horses in the country, and there was Clay Agent, who owned the stud that sired Don and Selim. When the old man went to town he would gather with his cronies, as he called them, back of Uncle Henry's store, and talk about horses and farming and cuss the cotton farmers.

Old Doc Adams would tell some of the biggest stories I ever heard. He said one time that he had a horse on the racetrack that ran so fast and threw his feet out so far in front of him that his hoofs cut his underlip. Then when the old Doc, who had a heavy gray beard, had finished telling one of his stories, Mr. Downing would tap the old man on the shoulder and say, 'Let us pray!' And the men would all roar. And the old Doc said, 'Believe it or not, gentlemen, every word of that story is true.'

This little bunch of radicals in the town liked to make fun of the bankers, especially Uncle Henry, who was getting richer and richer, so they would get Sam Ushery and Uncle Henry together and have Sam tell about some dreams he had had.

Sam Ushery was a full-blood Cherokee who had long black braided hair that hung down his back. He had a lot of dreams, or so he claimed, and strangely enough they all had Uncle Henry, or W. H., as he called him, in them.

The old man always enjoyed Sam Ushery's stories, most of all because he said Henry was getting to think too much about the almighty dollar and his wife and daughters were thinking too much about piling clothes on their backs. Some of Sam's stories went something like this:

'One night,' said Sam, 'I dreamed I died and went up to the pearly gates of heaven. Saint Peter stopped me and said, "Riding or walking?"

'I said, "Walking."

'Saint Peter said, "Sorry. Nobody can get in here unless he's riding."

'I turned around and started back, and a little ways down the road I met W. H. and told him what had happened.

'W. H. said, "I'll fix that — I'll get on your back, and when Saint Peter says, 'Riding or walking?' I'll say riding and we'll walk in."

'Well, W. H. got on my back and we went back to the pearly gates and Saint Peter said, "Riding or walking?"'

'W. H. said, "Riding."

'Saint Peter said, "All right, hitch your horse outside and come on in."

'And that's the way,' Sam Ushery concluded, 'that the white man treats the Indians.'

There would be loud guffaws all around, and when Uncle Henry said, 'I've got to be getting back to the bank,' the old man said, 'No, hold on. Sam is going to tell another story; he had two dreams last night.'

'Yes,' said Sam, 'I had another dream, and this time I actually did get into heaven. Well, I inquired around for my friends, and sure enough, there was the preacher here and the professor and old Doc Adams. I was afraid to bring it up on account of W. H. loving money so much, being afraid he hadn't got in, but finally I asked for W. H.

'"Oh, yes," they said, "W. H. is here, but you know, something funny happened. He ran up that long pole which goes clear to the top of the tabernacle and we can't get him down."

'"I know how to get him down," I said.

'"How is that?" they said.

'"Have you got a quarter?" I said.

'So they gave me a quarter and I took it and tapped on

the pole to attract W. H.'s attention and held it out so he could see it. When W. H. saw that quarter he slid down so fast it would make your head swim.'

Again all the men would burst into loud laughs, the old man loudest of all, and Uncle Henry would turn a little red.

The old man thought very highly of Doc Adams's judgment of horse flesh. He wanted to get the Doc's opinion on Don's saddle gaits. He had spent a lot of time that year training the colt. He had broken him to the saddle and got him so he wasn't so wild, but Don still had a lot of fire in him.

The colt was still ugly as a scarecrow, but he was beginning to develop some points I had overlooked. He held his head very high in the air. His eyes were bright and sharp and his mane was getting long and silky. His nose was very long; his head was narrow and his ears registered everything he saw. He was constantly on the alert. Although he had filled out some, his body was long and thin. His hips were not rounded, but steep, and his legs still gave the impression he was on stilts. Although Don looked as if a puff of wind would blow him over, and at rest looked ungainly and awkward, when he ran and skipped and played every movement was graceful.

One day we rode Don and Selim to town, and met Clay Agent and old Doc Adams down by the railroad crossing. The old man said, 'Son, ride down the road a ways and then ride him by so the Doc and Mr. Agent can see him.'

I rode the colt about three hundred yards down the road. Then I turned him around, headed him toward home, and put him into a regular smooth fox-trot. After a hundred yards or so I leaned over in the saddle and tightened the reins slightly. The colt glided into the prettiest single-foot you ever saw. I had got almost to the railroad track before I saw a train coming away down the track a mile or so. We had just crossed the track when I heard the whistle. Don always was afraid of trains. If you got him within a half-mile of one you were lucky.

I was just getting ready to put Don into the rack pace when he heard the train, and he quivered all over and doubled his speed. I had to tighten up on the reins to hold him down. He was frightened, but he didn't break his gait. I let him out a little. Mr. Agent and the Doc were a little way down the road. As we got closer to them I let the colt out more. He was feeling good. He was heading for home and he could hear the roar of the train coming down the track behind him. Then the train whistled again. We were almost even with Mr. Agent. The colt swept forward. I tightened the reins, afraid he would break his gait. I felt him flatten out, his long neck stretch forward, and I felt close to the ground and vaguely aware of the long legs beating the air like flails. I could see his front hoofs flashing under his neck and chin. I tried to pull him down, but even with the long curb bits I couldn't do so in the slightest.

It was three quarters of a mile before I could get that colt stopped; then I rode back to where Mr. Agent and the Doc were.

'Sam,' said Mr. Agent, 'that's the fastest piece of horse-flesh in the country.'

Old Doc Adams bubbled over. 'I was born and bred on the racetrack, and that colt will stand up with the best of 'em. He has the instincts and spirit of a racer.'

Old Doc Adams tried to get the old man not to break Don to work. 'Don't work that horse, Brother Mac,' he said. 'It would break his heart.'

'God intended horses to work. Of course that colt will work. He'll be pulling the plow along with the rest of the horses. Work, Doctor Adams, is the rule of life. It is the mainspring of our civilization. Horse-racing is all very well, but I wouldn't have a horse just for riding alone. I want an all-purpose horse. Now, that colt, of course, is not a draft type, but he'll be good for light work and he'll be a fine buggy animal.'

Old Doc Adams shook his head sadly. 'Doctor McDonald,' he said, 'you can't make a sow's ear out of a silk purse. You are an authority on most everything, but there is one thing I know more about than you do. I was born and raised on the racetrack. All my life horses have been my passion. I've trained 'em, bred, and doctored 'em. They are my life.

'There's just as much difference in horses as in people. Some are dull and stupid, some are fiery and sensitive, some are wild and proud, whose spirit will never be broken until they die. You might kill them, but you could never break their spirit. Some horses are born aristocrats. That colt was made to run. He knows it. I can see it in his eyes. He will never wear a collar. Now, you have trained these other colts; you have done a good job. I couldn't train them better myself. But for God's sake, don't work that colt. He is different from the others.'

'Now you listen to me,' said the old man. 'I'll have no drones on my place. My horses work, my boys work, my cows give milk, my land produces food for my family and my stock. For every living thing God has a use. For a horse or a boy not to work would upset the balance. All living things that eat must work. Work is the law of evolution. It is the rule of the universe. Those creatures who do not adapt themselves to it must die. They must give way before more efficient organisms. So my place must be according to God's plan. My little farm is a miniature universe where nothing is wasted, where we live on our good mother, the Earth, who in the aggregate gives us what we give her. For what we take from her we give back in another form. My cows eat grass and hay taken from the land, but their dung enriches the soil that supports them. A balance is struck. So it must be with other things. Those who do not work should not eat lest they deprive others of the fruits of their labor. That colt must work or I will dispose of him.'

'Very well, but you will see that I am right,' said Doc Adams.

The day came to break Don to the plow. The colt was now almost three years old and should have been broken before. Selim, only a year older, had been plowing nearly two years.

Don had thickened up some. He was not nearly so thin as he used to be. His hair and mane were fine and silky. He had as pretty a coat of sorrel hair as ever I saw.

One morning we put the plow harness on him and we drove him around the yard. He didn't like it much. The collar annoyed him and the clanking of the trace chains frightened him. When we put the blind bridle on him he tried to shake it off.

The next day we harnessed him again, and this time

fastened the trace chain to a single-tree and drove him around the yard some more. I held the single-tree so it wouldn't bump his heels and the old man drove him out into the orchard.

We drove Don around the orchard and I stopped to pick an Elberta peach and the single-tree slipped out of my hand. It hit Don on the fetlocks and he jumped about twenty feet — jumped so quick and so hard he jerked the old man down and dragged him about ten feet before he stopped.

'What did you drop the single-tree for?' yelled the old man. 'Do you want to ruin that colt?'

The next day we hooked Don up with Star and drove them around the field. After the mishap the day before he was very skittish and pranced around champing his bit.

'I don't think that colt will ever work,' I said. 'Doc Adams was right.'

'Don't you believe it. He'll be working fine in a month.'

Along toward noon we hooked Don and Star to the turning-plow and let them drag it around the field. I was surprised when Don didn't cut up much. We had been breaking land in that field and had a big piece laid off. The old man just drove the team around and around, cutting a swath about an inch wide. Don turned crossways a few times near the end, but I was leading him and got him straightened out. At the turn the old man dragged the plow around so the trace chains wouldn't hit Don's legs and so he wouldn't step out of the traces.

Before the day was out the old man was driving the team around the field without Don's being led. He gradually cut a little wider swath with the plow until the team was pulling about half a load.

The next day we repeated the process and the old man wasn't so careful about the trace chains. One time around the end Don stepped over one of the traces and it rubbed the inside of his leg.

Quick as a flash he kicked with one foot, not once, but several times in succession. I jumped to his head and backed him so that the trace became slack and didn't scrape his leg.

For a few days we didn't have any mishaps with the colt. But I noticed that he was inclined to walk too fast around the field ahead of the other horse so that he pulled most of the load. And when we put a load on him he got faster. The plow was light and he should have been able to pull half of a six- or eight-inch swath without any trouble. But if we cut over three inches with that little plow in the sandy ground, he began to lunge. I could see that he didn't like a collar, especially when it was pulled back hard against his shoulder.

It was the third or fourth day of labor for Don. There was a high wind which swept across the eight-acre field where we were plowing. My brother had one team on one side of the field and I was plowing Don and Star on the other. As I was turning around, the wind picked up a piece of paper and carried it square toward the team. I saw it coming and expected trouble because I had seen Don get frightened at such things before.

When the piece of paper came sailing toward the colt, he turned and jumped sideways. Some way he got his left forefoot over Star's hame. That was how high he jumped! This threw him off his balance and he fell flat on his side, but he was up in a flash.

The old man had been repairing one of his dams near-by. He came running. 'Hold on to those lines, son.'

He was at Don's head, talking to him, trying to keep hold of the bridle. Don seemed suddenly to have gone insane. He struck at the old man with his forefeet. He reared so high in the air I thought he would fall back. Each time he lifted the old man clear off the ground.

'Turn him loose!' I yelled. 'He will kill you.' But the old man would not, although Don continued to rear up and lunge from side to side.

Then the colt started kicking. Putting his head between his legs, he bucked for five or ten minutes. As he bucked, he jumped backward and his long legs cut the air over my head as I squatted down. I think he was trying to kill me.

It was an hour before we got him stopped. Even then he danced up and down.

All that day we tried to work him. Up one side and down the other of the field we would go. For a minute he would walk along quietly enough. Then something would happen; the trace chain would touch his hock at the turn and this would set him to kicking again. Then he would rip and rear for half an hour, doing everything but stand on his head.

I was glad when the end of the day came. We were all worn out and had done no work. For once, the old man was ready to rest. My mother begged him not to try to work that colt any more. But he had made up his mind.

'I don't know what's going to become of your papa,'

my mother said. 'Some day he is going to meet an immovable object. He has always been an irresistible force and now I'm afraid he's met his match. That colt is a whole lot like your father. Neither one will give up. He says that he has never been beaten. And how well do I know it! He has never really given in on an issue that he considered important.'

In the morning we put the kicking straps on Don and hooked him up with a big old gentle bay horse. That day was the same as the one before. We never went over three or four rounds without Don's throwing a fit.

He changed his strategy somewhat, though. He would act very gentle, then suddenly try to jerk loose from Charley, who had been holding his head. That left me with only one line, the left one, and away that colt went. Round and round he ran in a big circle, pulling the poor old bay after him. All I could do was to pull on the left line and watch him go.

Part of the time the plow was high in the air over the backs of the horses. Once it caught on a stump and jerked the colt flat. To make matters worse, the dogs got excited and Colonel, the bulldog, began jumping at Don's throat. The old man was yelling at the top of his voice, the two hands were shouting directions, and all was confusion.

When the plow caught on the stump, Don lunged and broke the single-tree. By that time I had got hold of the other line, and with the old man's help I held the colt down, and that was the end of that day.

The next was almost the same. The colt grew defiant, vicious. He adopted all sorts of stratagems to take us off our guard — to get away from the plowing he hated. His

spirit was unbroken. He was determined he would not
work, and the old man was determined that he should.

We finally got the field broken, but the other team did
the work. Don didn't turn any ground to amount to
anything.

We were going to the house. I was driving the old bay
and Don, with the plow dragging behind them. Charley
was leading the colt. We did not trust him for a minute.
The old man, walking a short way ahead of the team,
stopped to pick up a rock to put on one of his dams.
Don quickened his pace. When he approached the old
man, he laid back his ears and reared high into the air.
As he came down, he struck twice at the old man, first
with one foot and then the other. Although this happened
in a second, Charley and I were on our guard. I pulled on
the lines and Charley threw his weight on the lead rope
in his hand. Even so the colt would probably have killed
the old man if he had not jumped to one side. When Don
saw he had failed, he stood quietly.

The old man was in a rage. I had never seen him so
angry. Grabbing the bridle, he jerked Don's head down,
looked him in the eye. 'You no good drone,' he yelled,
'you would kill me!' His eyes narrowed to pinpoints. I
could see the muscles standing out on his jaws as he
ground his teeth. 'You no good drone,' he yelled, 'I'll
kill you!' The old man continued to stand there a few
seconds and glare at the colt. Then he turned without a
word and walked to the house.

We never worked Don again. The old man would have
sold him, but he had given him to my brother and it
would have broken his heart to have the colt taken away.

It was the same year that Selim got his foot cut, not long after that incident with Don. Selim didn't come up with the rest of the stock. We had stayed out of school to plow and had got the horses out early in the morning for the day's work. I walked all over that forty acres before I heard him nicker. The old man had rented a forty-acre pasture to keep the stock in. Down on the lower side of the pasture I found my horse.

'Come here, Selim,' I said, but he didn't come, just nickered again.

I went over to where he was standing by the fence with his head down. A short time before the old man had had some heavy barbed wire put all around the pasture. Selim had his foot over the lower strand and I could see the blood gushing out from either side. I managed to get his foot off the wire. It looked as if it was cut two-thirds off. He had evidently got hung up the night before and sawed back and forth on the wire all night long.

I left the colt because I saw he couldn't walk, and high-tailed it back to the house and told the old man what had happened.

'All right, son,' he said. 'You go get Mr. Agent. Ride Dude. You can get there quicker on him.'

I threw a saddle on Dude and kept him in a dead run all the way to town.

Clay Agent knew more about stock than anybody in the country. They said he could cure a horse or a cow when no one else could. He owned the best stud in the country, and everybody who wanted good saddle colts bred their mares to his stud.

That morning he was carrying a bucket of shelled oats

out to the barn when I ran up all excited and told him about Selim.

Mr. Agent was the most deliberate man I ever saw. He never got excited about anything. I was excited and kicked over the oats he had set down. He squatted down and picked up every grain and his only comment was, 'Spilled a few oats.' Then he fed Prince, the stud, and saddled up his horse and we rode back to the pasture.

When we got there the old man was waiting. 'Well, Clay, we'd better shoot this colt. I wouldn't give a cent for him. Too bad — he was the boy's horse.'

'Well, let's see,' said Clay. After he had dressed the wound and bound it up, he said, 'Well, we'll see.'

The old man kept asking if he thought the colt would get well or if we hadn't better shoot him, but Mr. Agent didn't answer. All he said was, 'I'll come out late this afternoon again.'

Twice a day for two weeks we dressed the colt's foot. We didn't move him because he couldn't walk a step. The wound looked to me like it was getting worse in spite of all the doctoring.

Finally I said, 'Mr. Agent, won't you please tell me if my colt is going to get well? It looks like his foot is rotting away.' Great chunks of dead flesh were beginning to slough off.

'He'll live, all right, but he may limp a little,' replied Mr. Agent. 'No, I wouldn't say that. He may be as sound as a dollar, but there'll be a scar and a ridge on his hoof. I wouldn't ever give up hope in animals or men. I've doctored 'em when I thought there was no chance. I wouldn't have given a nickel for your horse two weeks ago. Now I think he'll be all right. Maybe.'

Selim finally got well. Mr. Agent doctored him for about three months. When he was cured the old man asked me if I thought we ought not to do something for Mr. Agent.

'I should say so,' I said. 'He has saved my horse for me.'

The old man sat down and wrote out a check. 'You take this down to Clay and tell him that we realize that it would be impossible for us to pay him for his services, and that this check is merely a gesture to show our appreciation for what he has done.'

I rode to town and up to Mr. Agent's house. He was sitting on the back porch shelling peas. When I had made my speech, I handed him the check, which was made out for five dollars.

'Tell Mr. Mac,' said Mr. Agent in his slow drawl, 'that I accept this in the spirit in which it was given, not as payment for my services, but merely as a token of his esteem.'

13

REMEMBER YOUR OLD DADDY WAS ONE OF THE PLAIN PEOPLE

'I WANT to have a big family reunion this year. We haven't had one for a long time now,' the old man said one day.

'If the older children come and bring all their families, I don't know where we'll put them,' said my mother. 'Of course, we can stick them away somewhere, I guess.

'There's something that's been bothering me,' she went on. 'The house ought to be papered. I am really ashamed for the older children to see these bare walls.'

'Yes, it should be,' admitted the old man, 'but I'm afraid we can't afford it.'

My mother had tried to get the old man to paper the house for years, but he claimed he never had enough money. He didn't think it was so important, anyway. 'The outside of a house has got to be protected from the weather. What difference does the inside make? The house keeps us warm on the cold winter nights, that's the main thing,' he had said.

He had the house painted every two years. He said that would keep it from rotting. Our house was for that country quite an imposing structure. We had eight large rooms, four downstairs and four upstairs, and there was an enormous attic. Besides, there were two large porches, one in front and one in back. The roof of the front porch was supported by large white columns.

'I'll tell you what we'll do, wife,' the old man said. 'I'll build a new sleeping-porch in the back if you'll use your butter-and-egg money to pay for papering and canvasing the house.'

'Well, all right, Mr. McDonald,' my mother said a little reluctantly. She had been saving her money in the hope that she could buy a new set of furniture.

What we had was pretty old and dilapidated. The old man didn't believe in spending his money for furnishings. Most of the things had been purchased with my mother's money. All the money we made selling chickens, pigs, and vegetables my mother and we children got. But a large part of it we had to spend for various things in the house. Even then we had sizable bank accounts. Each of us had his own heifer and his own horse and saddle.

The money from the peach orchard the old man gave to my sister Beatrice. She would go down and engage peaches at the village grocer's and we boys would pick them and take them down to Sallisaw in the buggy and deliver them.

In a short time, men came out and started putting the canvas on the walls preparatory to papering them. The old man in the meantime had hired some carpenters to come out and build a large upstairs sleeping-porch. He was not satisfied to build just an ordinary porch, but had it completely glassed in, with windows all the way around. 'I want the children to have a good comfortable place to sleep,' he said. 'These frosted windows will keep the after-noon sun from beating in, and at night they can be raised to let the air in.'

After a while, all the work was completed and we began to get answers to our letters inviting the older children to come in for the family reunion.

The old man asked them to come in July because by then we should have the crops laid by and there wouldn't be so much work to do. The older children — Katherine, Mary, Foster, Dessie, and Effie — were scattered from California to New York and they had not, in my memory, all been together at our house. Occasionally we saw Sister Katherine, who lived in Arkansas, and Mary, who lived in Kansas City, but the others we had seen only once or twice in our lives. So it was a great thrill to us when they finally arrived.

All of them came but Dessie, who it seems was in Europe on business and couldn't get here. Her daughter, little Katherine, came however. Although she was my niece,

she was about as old as Beatrice. The husbands of Mary,
Katherine, and Effie came also.

The old man liked his sons-in-law but found something
wrong with each, partly, I suppose, to bolster his idea
that no man was good enough for his beautiful and talented
daughters.

'Jim is a fine fellow,' he would say, 'a hale fellow well
met, but no business man.'

We children liked Jim Gibson best of all the in-laws.
He was jovial and witty; complimenting mother on her
cooking and showing her a lot of attention in other ways.

'Now, Ed Smith is a brilliant fellow, a good money-
maker,' the old man said of Brother Edgar, 'but it's too
bad he's such a red-hot Republican.' And he would say
sadly, 'He's put those fool Republican ideas into Mary's
head. I'll be blessed if she's not worse than Edgar.'

This difference in politics almost caused a schism in the
family a time or two. Foster was a red-hot Democrat and
he taunted Mary occasionally about how Woodrow Wilson
had taken them to a cleaning.

Brother Edwin, I guess, had more in common with the
old man than the other sons-in-law, because he was a
Presbyterian preacher, but it was characteristic of the
old man that he found fault with him too. 'Edwin is a
brilliant scholar but a poor money-maker. He's too bookish. If he didn't preach such long-winded sermons he
could hold a church longer. Effie holds his churches together. She is the brains of the family.'

Cousin Jim, Uncle Henry's boy, brought some of the
kin out in his new car. He had one of the few cars in the
family. Although the old man hated cars worse than the

Devil, Jim was his favorite nephew. Jim ran Uncle Henry's big store and he gave the old man a new pair of shoes every year. The old man especially liked him for this and because his wife, Billy, was one of his favorite nieces. 'Jim certainly turned out well,' he would say. 'He was a little rollicky before he was married, but now he's a fine husband and father.'

Jim had several children, and the old man was very happy every time Jim and his wife had another baby. 'The McDonalds are a prolific bunch,' he would say. 'The Lord has blessed them with large families.'

'There's one thing I don't like, Jim,' he said one time. 'There's none of the kin named Allen. Why don't you name your next boy after Great-Great-Grandfather Allen McDonald?'

'Well, Uncle Jim,' said Jim, laughing, 'give us a little more time. I'll name the next one Allen; that is, if it's a boy.'

'That's fine, Jim. I'll hold you to your promise, and I'll tell you what I'll do. If you name your next boy after Great-Great-Grandfather Allen McDonald, I'll give you his walking-stick.'

That stick had been in the family for over a hundred years and was one of the old man's most prized possessions. The handle of it was made out of buckhorn and had been made shortly after the Revolution. I was certainly surprised when he offered to give it to Jim.

Jim was good as his word. He named his next boy Allen, and the old man got out the old walking-stick and had it painted and a new name plate put on it and gave it to Jim.

My brother and I took the young crowd out and showed them the crops and the horses and the other stock.

The year before, the old man had bred the mares to a jack, and Star and Nell had two fine mule colts. My niece, little Katherine, was mystified when she saw Jet, the mule colt, following its horse mother around.

'Where is the little mule's mother?' she asked.

'Standing right there,' I said, pointing to Star.

'But that is impossible. The little one is a mule and the mother is a horse,' she said.

'I can see there are a lot of things city folk don't know about a farm,' I said.

My brother and I were amazed at the greenness of the children. Some of them refused to believe that corn grew in the field. 'That's not corn,' they said. 'You get corn out of cans.'

When we saddled up and put them on horses, they almost fell off if the horses got out of a walk. The horses, on their part, soon got wise to the ignorance of the children and went any way they wanted to.

Everybody enjoyed himself, though. The children rode and wandered over the farm asking questions about everything, and the grown-ups got together and had long talks about the happenings of long ago. And at mealtime, everybody seemed to like all the good food.

The old man enjoyed eating and bragging about how we had raised everything on the farm. Sometimes he would stop in the middle of the meal and enumerate everything we had for dinner. Once, I remember, he counted thirteen vegetables and three or four different kinds of fruit. There were great plates of fried chicken, ham, and beef. Then

there were three or four kinds of cake in addition to the
ice cream.

'We raised all this except the flour and the salt and
pepper,' the old man said. 'I never had so much to eat or
was so hard up in my life.'

We made our own ice cream, and I have never tasted
any as good as that we had on the farm. We put real
cream in, not milk, and lots of eggs. I remember my sister
would go out on the back porch and skim the thickest
cream off six great pans of sweet milk that had been set
on the shelf the night before. Then she would mix the
ingredients, including beaten eggs, and put the mixture
in the freezer.

We had a big gallon freezer you turned by hand. My
brother and I would take turns at it until the cream was
frozen so hard you couldn't move the handle. Then we
would pack the freezer in ice until we were ready to eat
the ice cream.

Of all the older children, the one who appreciated my
mother's cooking most was Foster. He was a big man,
and he had a lot of the mannerisms of the old man. He
turned out his feet in the same way, and he spoke dog-
matically and in such authoritative tones that everybody
stopped to listen, even at family gatherings. He, too,
liked to eat, to talk about eating, and to consider how good
everything was in relation to its cost. But he had a habit
of swearing that was a source of embarrassment to my
mother and a great shock to us children.

He would sit at the table and eat enough for two or
three men, and my mother kept piling his plate up and he
went on stuffing himself and talking about how good
everything was.

'By God!' he would bellow, after he had to let out his belt several times, 'how do you make things so good, Mother? Jesus Christ!' he would say before she had time to answer, 'this is good. By God, I'm going to kill myself. By God, I sure am.' And he would grunt and bellow and laugh. 'Ah-ha, this is good, by God!'

'Oh, son,' said my mother, coloring up a little, 'you shouldn't use the Lord's name in vain.'

'Oh, that's all right,' Foster said with his mouth full. 'You always wanted me to get into the church. Well, you know I just joined and I've got a right to call on Jesus Christ. He's head of the church. Besides, it's all right to call on the Lord when you're in pain. By God, I'm sure in pain. My belly is going to bust if I don't stop eating.'

The old man didn't hear, or pretended not to hear, Foster's profanity. He was proud of him, as of the other children, and prone to overlook his faults. He was happy that Foster had recently joined the church.

'There's nothing really bad about Foster,' my mother would explain to us children. 'He worked around railroad men for twenty years and got into the habit of swearing and he just can't stop. He doesn't mean to be wicked. And he isn't at heart.'

According to the family, my mother always took up for Foster. He and the old man had not got along very well in the past and she had tried to make the rough places smooth. The old man was very stern and intolerant in his younger years, and Foster had something of the same fiery temperament. As a result, there was a clash of wills and my mother tried to make peace. She was successful to the extent that her stepson loved her dearly, and never a year passed that he didn't send her some remembrance, some gift at Christmas-time, and on her birthday and on Mother's Day.

'God threw the mold away when he made you, Mother,' he would say. 'By God, he did!'

He was devoted to the old man too. All the early differences had been forgotten and he always shed a few tears when he left. Because Foster occasionally visited us in our childhood, Beatrice, Worden, and I got a better impression of him and grew to know him better than the other children.

Sometimes the old man would say to my mother that her children would never make their place in the world as his had done. When he was in a bad humor, he taunted her about the success of the older children, prophesying failure for us. But my mother was not perturbed. 'There is no doubt in my mind, Mr. McDonald,' she would say, 'about the success of my children.'

On other occasions, the old man would brag to everybody about how brilliant all his children were. 'There is not a dullard in the whole bunch.'

Once in a while he boasted to the older children and to the kin how smart Beatrice, Worden, and I were.

'All of my children take to the farm like ducks to water. They can handle a fiery horse as well as I can.' He was especially proud of the way Beatrice could ride. He insisted that women should ride sidesaddle and borrowed Aunt Jennie's saddle for Beatrice. Although Nell was pretty fiery and would still run away at the drop of a hat, Beatrice could handle her like a veteran cowpuncher. She would put Nell into a gallop and sit on that sidesaddle just as much at ease as if she were in a rocking-chair. Worden and I rode everything on the place — calves, colts and horses with and without bridles, surcingles, or saddles, but we never could quite understand how Beatrice could sit that mare so pretty sideways.

My brother Worden was especially skillful with horses. For one thing, he had not the slightest fear of a horse, no matter how wild and vicious it was. After he was about ten years old, he broke most of the colts in his own way without the knowledge of the old man.

The summer of the reunion the old man took Foster and the three brothers-in-law around the place, showing them his land, his crops, and his dams. When they approached our little bunch of horses grazing in the north pasture, the old man said, 'The boys help me break the colts. They have learned a lot about horses in the last few years. You see that filly there,' he said, pointing to Dixie, who was Star's second colt. 'We're going to break her to ride pretty soon. She'll make a fine little saddle and buggy animal.'

'Do the boys break the horses by themselves?' asked Foster.

'Oh, no,' said the old man. 'They couldn't break a colt without my help.'

Worden, who had been listening to the conversation, slipped away from the crowd and went over and grabbed Dixie's mane and swung himself lightly on her back.

'Boy, boy!' yelled the old man, 'what are you doing? That colt will run away and kill you.'

But Worden just laughed and hit Dixie on the rump with his straw hat and she galloped away. Worden had been riding that colt on the sly for a couple of months and he couldn't resist the temptation to show off.

'Well, can you beat that? It seems I can't keep up with the boys now,' said the old man, not a little proudly.

That night at the supper table he said, 'How would you folks like to go to Sallisaw Creek tomorrow? You can go in swimming if you like. At least the children can.'

The next morning Worden and I hooked up the team and all the McDonald clan loaded into the John Deere wagon, which looked as good as new because the old man had kept it in the dry. We put in hay and covered it with blankets so everybody would have a soft spot to sit on. The old man drove the team and Worden and I rode our horses. Worden had just got a new saddle and he rode Don, of course, and I rode Selim. Don, as usual, put on an exhibition. He danced off on his hind legs, only occasionally putting a front foot to the ground.

My mother and sister drove Pet to the buggy. Pet was a little pony the old man had bought especially for my mother. Since the Dude runaway he was afraid for her to drive one of the younger, more fiery horses.

That year Uncle Henry had given us his buggy — he had just bought a car and had got rid of his horse. It was a considerable improvement over our old ramshackle cut-under buggy. It was fairly new and had a top and side curtains to keep the sun and rain out.

We planned our outing on the banks of big Sallisaw Creek. There we took out the horses and hitched them to a tree and gave them some hay to munch.

All the young folk went in swimming. The old man took a little swim too. He had a bathing-suit that came down almost to his ankles. 'This new-fangled bathing-suit of mine is a little immodest,' he said, 'but anyway it is a lot better than most people wear. It's scandalous now how young people go in swimming practically naked. They might as well not have on any clothes at all.'

In the afternoon, after we had our swim we spread the dinner on the ground and ate. Before we began the old man blessed the food, and because it was such a special occasion he prayed for ten or fifteen minutes.

After the older children had been there a few days it was decided that the kin at Sallisaw and Fort Smith should be invited out for a big get-together. There was some talk among the womenfolk of what to wear, and it was found that my mother didn't have a decent dress to her name.

The older daughters were aghast. 'Why, Mother,' Mary said, 'you are almost ragged. What on earth is the matter with Papa that he doesn't see that you get proper clothes?'

'Oh, your Papa doesn't think clothes are important,' replied my mother. 'Anyway I have my own money.'

'Well, why haven't you bought at least a good dress and hat?' asked Mary.

'Well, it seems there's always something needed for the house and I just haven't got around to it.'

'What's the matter with that dress you've been wear-ing to Badger?' asked the old man, who had overheard the conversation. 'Why, that dress is as good as my mother ever had. That's one trouble with the modern generation. All people think of now is style. Style is ruin-ing the world.'

'Just ignore Papa,' said Mary. 'He thinks an old dressing-sack with a string tied in the middle is good enough to wear to church.'

The result of this conversation was that the older children all chipped in and bought my mother a completely new outfit. She probably had more clothes than at any time since she had married the old man. Foster, Mary, Katherine, and Effie together contributed a new dress, a new hat, new shoes, and new underwear.

The next Sunday afternoon, the time set for the big reunion, the kin began to arrive. Uncle Henry, Uncle Clayton, Uncle Green, Aunt Alice, and their numerous children and grandchildren gathered in our big living-room and on the front porch. Children sat on the stairs and in the doorways and in the old man's study, which adjoined the living-room. There were McDonalds everywhere — young, middle-aged, and old; little, middle-sized, and big.

The next day the reunion began to break up. Most of the kinfolk had to get back to their jobs and businesses and they started packing their things.

'Before you children leave,' said the old man, 'we want to have a little service and thank God for these pleasant times. It may be a long time before we have such a reunion as this.'

So that afternoon after a big dinner, we all gathered in the big dining-room. My sister played the piano and we all crowded around and sang songs. Then the old man got out the Bible and read a few verses. And then he prayed:

'O God, our Father in heaven, look down on us here gathered together to worship Thee and thank Thee for this reunion.

'Bless all these families here, and may prosperity and happiness shine on them.

'We thank Thee, O Lord, for all the good things we have eaten here. We thank Thee for this house and this farm which is hallowed ground blessed by Thee to give nourishment to our bodies that we may worship Thee in spirit and in truth.

'And bless, O Lord, not only this home but all the homes represented here. May they be blessed by large families and bountiful tables that they may carry on their work and live useful, purposeful lives dedicated to the service of our Lord, Jesus Christ. May the members of the McDonald family become, as once a chosen people became, as countless as the grains of sand.

'Bless each and every McDonald. May he put aside the fleshpots and temptations of this world and always keep his feet in a godly path. May he never stray from the path of virtue, and if he succumbs a little now and then to the temptations of the Devil, may he rise up like David and slay the giant evils that hem him in on all sides in this wicked world.

'For we know, O Lord, this is a wicked world, and we know all of us will be beset by temptations and many of these temptations will appear to be harmless pleasures. May each of us resist all these clever stratagems of the Devil. May we be given a keen eye, that will aid us to send the Devil slinking back away to his cesspool of iniquity.

'And may none of my children or my children's children become puffed up with pride and worldliness because they are blessed by material things. May they always remember their old daddy and their old daddy's daddy who was one of the plain people.

'We know that God will not be mocked with worldly success. We know that it is in the things of the spirit that we really prosper. Until we conquer our spirits we have lost all though we gain the whole world.

'I pray that our family may become strong in spirit and in truth, and that the McDonald family may be known as a godly family, and that it may set an example not only to the community but to the whole world. Amen.'

14

THAT WATER IS RUINING MY LAND
AND YOURS TOO

OLD man Cassidy had ten acres adjoining the north field, and they were being washed all to pieces. The land was originally pretty good, particularly the lower end. But every year our land got better and his got worse. Anybody could see that.

One day the old man walked Cassidy all over our farm and showed him his dams and his rock walls and his good crops. When they got to the lower side of the north field the old man stopped and pointed up the hill.

He looked at the long slopes that ran together and formed a draw in between. About thirty feet apart all the way up the draw were rock dams, and on the lower side was a rock wall three feet or so wide clear across the field. You could see the land rising all the way up the draw because the dirt had filled in behind each dam until it was six inches to a foot higher than the land behind it. The rows ran on the contours of the hill, and the pea vines were a dark green. In front of the rock wall the wash had filled in until our land was a foot and a half higher than old man Cassidy's.

'Look at that land,' said the old man. 'Four years ago you said it wasn't worth cultivating. I got a good crop of oats off it and the peas will be ready to pick in a few weeks. We'll pick what we need and then we'll make hay of the vines. I may not need all the vines. I'll turn the hogs and stock in on what we don't need.'

The old man always kept plenty of cowpea seed for his own use and some to sell. He sold thirty or forty bushels a year to the neighbors at five dollars a bushel. Nobody else picked and threshed his peas. It was too much trouble. The old man always had plenty of pea hay. He said that it was especially fine for milk cows in the winter. He kept all his hay in the dry. Not a drop of water ever fell on it if he could help it. Sometimes when a shower came up all hands and the cook turned out and got the hay under shelter. Then if it wasn't cured enough, we'd have to scatter it around the place. Although he sometimes put his hay in the barn before it was entirely cured, it never moulded. He had a system of ventilation in the barn. There were poles run through at intervals and parallel to each other. The hay was thrown over the poles so that there were air holes underneath.

Cassidy looked up the long hill at the draw with the dams and then he turned and looked at his field. 'Brother Mac, you are the damnedest dam-builder in the whole damn country. But I ain't got time to be hauling so much rock. You see that gully? Why, it would take a thousand loads of rock to fill it. I ain't stout. I can't be lifting them big rocks anyway.'

'It wouldn't take a thousand loads of rocks,' said the old man. 'Let's see. I'd put about eight dams in that biggest gully. Of course with the gully that deep it would take about a wagonload to each dam. I'll tell you what I'll do. If you'll put in those dams I'll furnish you a hand to help you lift the big rocks.'

I could see the old man was getting enthusiastic. He hated gullies worse than he hated the Devil, and he had looked at Cassidy's biggest gully for a long time, watching it grow and eat out and undermine the land. 'Then you could put a ditch here by the fence to take care of the surplus water. You could build little dams in the small gullies and you could run your rows on the contour of the hill to take care of the sheet wash. You shouldn't ever put cotton on that land. It is too hard on it. Cotton has been the ruination of the South. The American farmer is digging his economic grave by wasting his land.'

The old man went on for some time like this, but I could see old man Cassidy wasn't much interested. 'Brother Mac,' he said, and he wiped the amber off his lip, 'your idees are good, but not for the likes of me. I couldn't do all that extry work. I am rather poorly with my asthmy, and I have to raise cotton. How would I get money at the bank if I didn't? I got to have money to raise a crop and live on till I sell my cotton. You are well fixed. You can make all these improvements, but I ain't got the money.'

'Well, why don't you run your rows with the lay of the land and not up and down the hill?' asked the old man.

'I don't like point rows. I can't be turning my cultivator round every twenty feet. Why, if you was to run rows across the hill here you wouldn't get no work done at all — you would be turning round all the time.'

'Well,' said the old man, getting a little vexed, 'you could build those dams. I told you I'd furnish you a hand to help you.'

'Brother Mac,' said Cassidy, 'that-air water has got to go somewhere. Why not in that gully?'

The old man snorted. As he turned and stamped off toward the house I heard him mutter, 'Stupid fool!'

In his walks over the farm the old man got so he'd stop and look at the Cassidy ten acres more and more. Every time he looked at that big gully he seemed to get angry. It *was* a big gully. It just seemed to spring up out of the ground from nowhere right below our land. It ran about twenty-five yards from the fence almost straight down through Cassidy's land. The strip east of the gully was full of blackberry bushes and sassafras sprouts. We used to go down every year and pick blackberries in that thicket. In some places the underbrush was so heavy you couldn't ride a horse through it. This big gully ran on down the field, and where the land flattened out it got shallower, and you could see the sand that had been washed down on the good land in the lower end of the ten acres.

This end was flat and poorly drained and had a lot of swamp grass in it. In a wet year any crop that was planted there drowned out.

West of the gully old man Cassidy cultivated in cotton every year. The cotton never was much account, though. He never made over a bale and a half on the whole field.

Cassidy never broke his land. In May he would take his lister and throw up ridges, using last year's cotton rows for a furrow. He dragged the ridges down and then planted the cotton. The part of the field between the gully and the fence he let lie out.

More and more the old man walked down to the lower side of the eight-acre piece and looked at Cassidy's land. One day he climbed over the fence and walked up and down between the stunted rows of cotton, talking to himself. I heard him mutter something about the foundation of civilization's being undermined. Then he turned to me.

'Son,' he said, 'we'll buy this land. We need more land anyway.'

'But this land is poor and thin,' I said. 'Besides, old man Cassidy is so contrary he probably won't sell it.'

'He'll sell,' said the old man, and his lips set in a firm line and the muscles in his jaws showed the way they did when he gritted his teeth. I knew then he would have that land, because when once he made up his mind about something he never changed it.

The next day Cassidy came over to borrow a hame-string. The old man always kept a supply on hand. He and Cassidy got to talking about the land and crops. 'My land ain't good like yours, Brother Mac. It washes so bad. And my crops is poor. That last big rain washed out a lot of cotton on the north side of my field.'

'You're right,' said the old man. 'Your land is awful sorry. Some of it is not worth the taxes on it. It'd pay you to let that north ten go back for taxes.'

'Oh, I wouldn't do that,' said old man Cassidy. 'I wouldn't let it go for taxes. I might sell it, though.'

The old man laughed. 'Who'd buy it?'

'Why don't you buy it, Brother Mac? You said the other day you needed more land.'

'I need some good land. Well, we've got to get back to the field and finish pulling fodder. My daddy always saved his fodder. A good bundle of fodder will keep a horse from getting the thumps in hot weather.'

The old man never let his horses have much green stuff when they were plowing, especially in corn that was waist-high or over. He plowed his corn a month after the neighbors had. I've seen them lay their corn by when it was hip-high with straight shovels or solid sweeps. 'Corn,' he would say, 'has an extensive root system. It has to have lots of moisture. Look at the plow of a farmer who socks his plow into the bean next to the corn. You'll see thousands of roots hanging on the plow. The farmer who does that will lose his corn in a drouth.'

The neighbors couldn't understand why the old man's corn stood the drouth. Theirs would twist and burn, and the hill farmer was lucky if he got even a few nubbins. But the old man always made corn, drouth or no drouth.

In the first place, he turned his land deep so it would hold the moisture longer. Then he prepared a fine bed, and after the corn was up he plowed it every eight days. The other farmers waited for a rain before they plowed, but not the old man. He was a fanatic on raising corn. When it got up about knee-high he quit using shovels and started in with solid sweeps, and later with open sweeps, and later with big buzzard sweeps that barely scratched the surface. He had a theory about holding the moisture in time of drouth that took him an hour to explain. But nobody listened. The other farmers went on plowing their corn in the same old way. We didn't listen to him either. What was the use, when we had heard it so many times?

The old man said that if you kept the surface of the ground stirred it would break the capillary continuity and hold the moisture. He kept doing this in time of drouth until the corn was in silk and tassel.

One reason the old man's ideas didn't go over so well was that it took so much work to put them in practice. The neighbors thought it was foolish to pull fodder. It was a lot of trouble. We had to pull it in the hottest weather and tie it in hands, and then about dusk when the dew had begun to fall, go out and tie four hands into one bundle. If you tried it before dusk the blades were so brittle that they would tear all to pieces.

'Brother Mac, you shore do like work,' said Cassidy. 'Why, you can get hay a lot easier than that.'

'Cassidy, I heard you had been buying some hay,' said the old man. 'I have never bought a bale of hay and I never expect to.'

'Seems like my medder didn't turn out so good on account of the drouth,' said old man Cassidy. 'Brother Mac, if you hear of anybody that wants to buy my land, let me know. I'd sell cheap.'

'Any price would be high for that land,' said the old man. 'Come, boys, it's burning daylight; we've got to get that fodder pulled before night.'

Cassidy came back a few days later to borrow another hamestring. I wondered why the old man didn't ask him about the other one he had borrowed. But he didn't mention it and seemed glad to lend him another one. He and Cassidy got to talking. I thought maybe the old man would mention the ten acres, but he didn't.

Cassidy hung around quite a while. As he was leaving he said, 'You know, Brother Mac, I was looking over that ten acres this morning and it's a lot better than I thought it was. Part of it, if it was cleaned up, would be good land.'

'Why don't you clean it up?' said the old man.

'Brother Mac, why don't you buy that land? You need it to fill out your farm.'

'No, I don't need it.'

'Brother Mac, what will you give me for the ten acres?'

'Well, I don't need it, but just to help you, I might take it off your hands. I tell you what I'll do. I'll pay the back taxes on it and pay for the deed and abstract.'

Old man Cassidy was an easy-going old fellow who hardly ever got riled up, but I could see this made him angry. 'You are a preacher and you are trying to rob me.'

'Why, Cassidy, you know that land isn't any good. I just want to help you out.'

'You want to help me out, all right — help me into the poorhouse. Now, Brother Mac, why don't you make me an offer?'

'I never like to price another man's stuff. If you want to sell it, put a price on it.'

'I'll take five hundred dollars,' said Cassidy.

'You misunderstood me. I didn't want a price on your whole farm.'

'Well, I'll take four hundred dollars for the ten acres, and you pay the back taxes.'

'Cassidy, this heat must have affected your mind. That's not bottom land.'

'With a little improvement,' said Cassidy, 'it would be fine land. There is a fine spring on the lower side. Don't forget that.'

'You mean that hog wallow? That's not a spring. I'll tell you, Cassidy, the best I'll do. I won't go a cent higher. I'll give you fifty dollars and pay the taxes.'

'Now, Brother Mac, you and me has always been good friends. You want me to give my land away. That land is worth three hundred dollars if it's worth a penny, and I'll not take a cent less.'

'We have been neighbors a long time and I shouldn't let my friendship for you sway my business judgment, but I am going to offer you, against my better judgment, a hundred dollars. That's absolutely the best I'll do. Well, boys, we've got to get back to the field.'

Cassidy went on home grumbling to himself, and the old man was in an unusually good humor for several days. He went down and looked over the ten acres again when he was sure Cassidy had gone to town.

A week passed, and the old man seemed to get worried. He looked down toward Cassidy's place several times a day and frowned. Then one day something got the matter with the mowing machine and he sent me over to Cassidy's to get him to come and help fix it.

'Old man Cassidy doesn't know anything about a mower,' I said.

'You never mind. Do what I tell you,' said the old man sharply.

When Cassidy got there, he looked the mower over and began telling how much he knew about machinery. 'Yes, I know you are a natural mechanic,' said the old man. 'This blade seems to be stuck some way and won't work back and forth as it should.'

Cassidy didn't know anything about machinery, but he thought he knew everything. He and the old man triggered around the machine, worked the blade back and forth, and rolled the wheels a few times and the blade started working as it should.

'I thought you could fix it,' said the old man.

'Never did see anything I couldn't fix.'

'How about a cold glass of buttermilk?'

'I reckon I never did get enough of your good woman's buttermilk. I was just telling the woman the other day, Mis' Mac makes the best buttermilk of any woman in the country.'

'Sonny,' said the old man, 'you go get us some of your mother's good cold buttermilk. We'll lay off this afternoon. It's too hot to work.' I shall always remember that day because it was the only time in the ten years we lived on the farm that it got too hot to work.

That night at supper the old man was beaming. 'Well, boys, I just bought the Cassidy ten.'

The old man was a hard worker, but I have never seen him work so hard as he did that year on the Cassidy land. It was August when he bought it, and we hoped that he would wait until the worst hot weather was over before he started to work on it.

The old man began on the thickets along the gully. He hired two extra hands and set them to cleaning the place up. He had all the blackberry bushes and second-growth stuff cut out. He had one hand dig a ditch along by the fence down the hill and he and two others, after the brush was cleared out, did the hauling. Of course, my brother and I worked too.

When the brush was cut we piled it in the deepest part of the gully. Then we built eight big dams about twenty-five yards apart. I have never seen the old man take such pains. For the major wall he got the biggest rocks he could find and placed them all carefully. Sometimes he would show his hands how to build a dam and go round to superintend the other work. When he returned he would look at the dam, find something wrong with it, and tear it out and build it himself. He carried a sledgehammer in the wagon to break the rocks so they would all fit into place. The approaches extended back twenty feet from the major wall. Some of them had ten or fifteen loads of rock in them. When he had finally completed a dam and had got it just as he wanted it he would 'hist' his foot on the wagon hub and give a lecture on the soil.

'The Scotch,' he said, 'have contributed a great deal to conservation of the soil. There is no doubt in my mind that Jefferson got a lot of his ideas from them. It is natural of course that the Scotch should have been conservationists since they had a very poor country and since they were foremost in everything else.'

The hands didn't pay any attention to his lectures, but they enjoyed the rest anyway. Although the old man was getting along toward seventy at the time, he could work down any hand I ever saw. After four or five days the new hands quit. They couldn't stand the work. Even Charley threatened to take out. He said he wasn't going to kill himself for no dollar a day.

After the big dams were made the old man built a lot of little ones in the smaller gullies. He got some new hands and they finished digging the ditch which ran along the fence through the ten acres and divided it in half. Three acres of the ten were pretty good land and the old man planned to raise corn there. He built another fence, dividing the east five acres.

In the spring we got Uncle Josh Choate to help us set out Bermuda grass in the remaining two acres, and the old man built a gate between this field and our own grass pasture. The year before we had set out Bermuda in the calf pasture and the upper two-acre piece north of the garden. We took an old axe and chopped the Bermuda into blocks about four inches square, then slipped a straight spade under them to break loose the bottom rocks. Then we threw them onto the wagon.

The old man prepared his ground very carefully for Bermuda. He turned the ground and harrowed it three or four times so it would be finely pulverized. Then he laid off rows with a Georgia stock and a bull-tongue. We walked along behind the plow, dropping the seeds and mashing them down with our feet.

Uncle Josh was the slowest worker I ever saw. When he came dragging out to the field with the sun two hours high the old man would say, 'Look at Uncle Josh. Sight behind this post to see if he's moving.'

Uncle Josh thought people were all wrong for working so hard. 'I would rather sit in the shade and eat strawberries.'

The white man, as Uncle Josh figured, had ruined a fine country. 'Work, work, work. I'm sick and tired of hearing about work. When I work I take my time, but when Brother Mac works he tries to kill himself.'

'Boys,' he said, 'the Indians had the best way of life. They really enjoyed life. They hunted and they fished, and they didn't wear themselves out working for ungrateful children. I'm glad I haven't got any children to worry me to death. That's all children do — worry their parents. I believe in taking my time about everything. I don't even go to the privy as often as other people. One time I didn't have an action for nine days — yes, sir, nine days.'

'How did you feel, Uncle Josh?' I asked.

'Felt fine, felt fine. But you can't tell some people anything. Brother Mac is working himself into an early grave. What's the use? Rome wasn't built in a day.'

Uncle Josh spat slowly and wiped his lip with his hand. Then he got a sod out of the wagon and squatted down in the furrow and pressed the damp earth around it. 'Now this grass will do better than just stepping on it.' He packed the dirt around the sod like it was a sweet potato plant.

'Yes sir, I told Charity, I said, "It's not everybody could go nine days without an action. That would kill an ordinary man." Felt fine. In fact, I don't recall that I ever felt better.'

Uncle Josh was long and stringy and it took him quite a while to unfold himself and go over to the wagon and get another sod.

'You boys,' said Uncle Josh, 'have to work too hard. Why, when I was a boy all I had to do was to hunt and fish. These hills were full of deer and wild turkeys, all kinds of game. Yes, the good old days are gone.'

'Uncle Josh,' said the old man, who had walked over to where we were, 'if you'd work more and talk less you might get more Bermuda set out. I've set three rows to your one.'

'Rome wasn't built in a day,' was all Uncle Josh said, but he didn't have much to say the rest of the day.

After we got the Bermuda set, the old man had a lane built down to the spring between the two fields. He made his fences out of good, stout hog wire and three or four barbed wires. There was an old hog wallow down at the lower end of the field where water stayed most of the year. The old man cleared this hole, dug down about six feet, and walled it up. Then he enclosed about a fourth of an acre that he called the playground and put a big trough by the spring and ran a spout from it through the fence. In that way he kept plenty of water for the stock at all times. I used to go down about daylight every morning and fill the trough.

Ben Trimble lived right across the road from the spring and he could holler louder than any man I ever heard. Ben was a good worker and a good man, the old man said, but he could cuss louder and longer than any man in the country.

'Pity about Ben being so wicked,' said the old man. But I noticed he liked him fine anyway — a lot better than a lot of people who went to church and were so lazy they let their families starve.

'Ben is a good provider,' said the old man. 'A man who won't work, who'll lie around and let his family go hungry, ought to be taken to the woods and be bucked down over a log, have his pants lowered and a big board applied to his setter. Lots more people will go to hell for not working during the week than for cussing or working on Sunday.'

There were several gullies that ran down through the good land that the old man wanted to put corn in. He built several dams to stop the wash and dug a ditch alongside the fence where part of the gully ran. The water came from old man Cassidy's land on the east side. Just before it got to our land it spread out over the field and ran through the fence and onto our land. Part of the land was washed clear down to the subsoil, leaving the surface hard and slick.

'I'll get Cassidy to build a dam along the dividing fence and turn the water into the ditch so it'll stop that water,' said the old man.

The next time Cassidy came over to borrow something the old man took him down to the field and explained his plan.

'Brother Mac, that-air water has got to go somewhere.'

'But that water is ruining my land and yours, too.'

'Well, I ain't going to build no dam for you,' said Cassidy. 'You build all the dams you want to. Dams is all you think about. You got the dam fever. But I'll be damned if I build any damn dams on this damn land.'

The old man's face got grim. His steel-gray eyes got

small and sort of three-cornered. He gritted his teeth and I could see the muscles standing out like cords on his jaws.

'Very well,' he said, 'you ignorant, illiterate, churn-headed fool! But it's you and farmers like you that are ruining this country. Yes, ruining it — world without end. This country is going to rack and ruin because of improvident farmers. What you need is to be taken out and bucked down over a log. Now you get off my place and stay off.'

The old man didn't speak to Cassidy for five years. Not long after that Cassidy went around to Uncle Green and talked to him about making up with the old man.

Uncle Green said, 'Well, Jim, you've got to make allowance for some people.' But it didn't do any good.

'I'll have nothing more to do with that churn-headed fool,' said the old man.

15

YOU'VE GOT TO FEEL IT OR THERE'S NO REAL RELIGION

THE job of a country preacher like the old man was much harder than that of a city preacher who had only one church. The old man not only had the churches at Dwight Mission, Badger Lee, and Price's Chapel to look after, but he preached occasionally at other places.

Usually he preached at one place not more than once a month, but he made it his business to know the people in the community and to see that they got out to church on Sunday. He also looked after their farming interest.

He never failed to compliment the good farmer and he always insisted on seeing the cellar and the garden and the smokehouse. If the farmer had none of these things he rebuked him sharply and referred to him afterward as being no account.

He believed that the Lord looked with favor on the hard-working farmer. 'The Lord will smile when he looks down and sees the smokehouse full, but when he sees the man sitting around wearing out the seat of his pants without a dust of flour in the house, his wrath will be great.'

One thing that made the old man such a good church organizer and so popular among the country people was his remarkable memory. He knew the name of every man, woman, and child in Sequoyah County — white and Indian. He was very popular with the mothers of the community, not only because he remembered the babies' names but also because he always called attention to some distinguishing characteristic of the child. 'That boy,' he would say to some proud mother, 'will make a great preacher. He's a handsome fellow, too; looks like his mother,' he would say roguishly. 'Good thing he didn't inherit his daddy's looks.'

The old man condemned the snobbishness of city preachers. 'Some of these modern preachers,' he said, 'think they've done their job for the Lord when they prepare a fine scholarly sermon that nobody can understand and shake hands with the brothers and sisters as they go out. Why, I've known lots of them who didn't know the name of a single child in the community. A preacher who is not liked by the children is no preacher.'

Another way that he got in well with the women was

to compliment their cooking. He had an enormous appetite, and he would eat as much as three normal men when he went visiting.

In spite of the old man's familiarity with the people, he commanded a great deal of respect. People stood a little in awe of him. The rowdy boys in the community were no exception.

In a good many places in Oklahoma the new preacher had to go through experiences like the new teacher in a country school. Sometimes the community toughs would get together and threaten to whip him. They would gallop their horses by when services were going on, and frequently they would break into the church building and desecrate it in some way. But the old man never let the rowdy boys or anything else interfere with his preaching.

More often than any other one of the family, I accompanied the old man into the backwoods when he preached. Quite frequently the road was too rough or the creek was too high to drive the buggy, so the old man and I went horseback riding, he riding Nell and I riding Selim.

I remember one time I went with him to Dwight Mission when Sallisaw Creek was filled from bank to bank. We stopped at Uncle Jack Rider's to ask about the high water.

'Git down, git down, Brother Mac,' said Uncle Jack, when we drove up to the gate in our old tacky buggy. 'Git down and come in,' he said.

'No, Uncle Jack, I haven't time. I have to preach at Dwight today.'

'Well, now,' said Uncle Jack, 'well, now, I don't know about that. I heered the river was up right smart. I don't think they're crossing at McCoy. Wouldn't try it. Hooks came by this morning and said it swum his horse. There comes Hooks now.'

Hooks was one of the Adair boys, one of the main families. He was one of the best-mannered boys in the community.

'Hooks, how's the water this morning?' asked Uncle Jack.

'The highest I ever seen,' said Hooks. 'Reckon it'd swim a horse easy by now.'

'Wouldn't cross, Brother Mac, wouldn't cross. Better sit down and rest a spell,' said Uncle Jack.

'No, no, I'll be getting on. I don't want to miss my appointment. I'll go down and look at the creek.'

When we got down to the creek the old man shook his head. The water was over some of the second bottom. 'I never have seen it so high.' Hooks had ridden back to the creek with us. 'There is a ford two miles up that isn't so bad, Brother Mac,' he said. 'You might try that.'

'Well, Cargin, I believe I will. This would swim an elephant. We could try it, but the current might wash us downstream and turn the buggy over. This boy can't swim.' He always called Hooks Cargin, because that was his real name.

We drove down to the other ford and looked at the water there. The channel was narrower but the water looked swift and black and deep.

'Well, I believe we'll try it here.'

'I'm afraid we'll get drowned,' I said. 'Maybe we ought not to cross.'

'Nonsense, boy. I've got to keep my appointment.'

'Get up, Selim.' We were driving Selim to the buggy now. Thanks to Mr. Agent his cut foot was as strong as the others and he didn't limp a bit. There was a bad scar, though, and a heavy ridge that went clear down the side of his hoof. He was a powerful horse with deep shoulders and a short back. He never lay down when there was a heavy load but pulled more than his share. His stay chains were always tight when we had him hooked to the wagon. He didn't get excited and prance around like Nell.

He seemed a little afraid to hit that ugly water, though, and I didn't blame him. The old man slapped the lines and he waded in. It was all right until we got nearly to the middle of the stream. Then the water suddenly got deeper and I could tell the horse was struggling to keep his footing, but pretty soon he couldn't and he started swimming. The buggy bed was filled with water and we had to lift our feet to keep them from getting wet. Downstream the buggy was swept until we were headed almost upstream. Selim was swimming as hard as he could but he wasn't making much headway.

'Steady, boy, steady,' said the old man, slapping the lines and bracing his foot on the dashboard, which was almost covered with water. The whirling water was almost over the seat. 'Sonny, grab the horse's tail when I cut him loose from the buggy,' he yelled, getting out his knife.

'We'll all be drowned, horse and all, and I can't swim a lick,' I thought. A lot of things went through my mind during those seconds when the horse was struggling against that muddy angry water.

Suddenly Selim got a footing; the water had carried

him downstream to where it was shallower. He stopped almost exhausted. You could hear his breathing above the swirling noise of the water.

The old man had his knife out ready to cut the traces.

'Maybe we can get out now without losing the buggy,' said the old man. 'Giddap Selim,' and he headed the horse toward the shore.

'It wouldn't have done any good to cut the traces. The shaft straps would have had to be cut too. Besides, you didn't need to cut them — you could have unhooked them,' I said. Now that the danger was over I saw what could have been done.

We resumed our journey to Dwight, which was several miles farther on.

The old man got to talking about early church history and how the Cumberland Presbyterian Church was started.

'Our people were active in the early religious movement that swept over the South after 1800. The old churches had become worldly. They had lost the spirit. They had become stiff-necked. The city preachers had become full of pride.

'The Presbyterians became to a great extent like the Episcopalians. They became formal and snobbish. They looked down on the poor. They didn't carry on any missionary work. They grew worldly and cut themselves off from the people.

'Then came the great religious awakening. The people in the backwoods began to hold great revivals. Camp meetings were held and people would come for miles and the meetings would go on for weeks and the people, shut off so long from any genuine religion, wrestled with the Devil. They felt their religion, at last. And that's what true religion is. You've got to feel it or there's no real religion.

'A part of this great religious upsurge, this revolt against the formalism of the old rich and snobbish churches, was channelized in the Cumberland Presbyterian Church. It was a young church that was started a little after 1800. Our people joined it in the early days and have been active in it ever since.'

'Why did you leave the Cumberland Church?' I asked.

'In unity there is strength,' he answered. 'I never looked on my church as a sectarian sort of thing. The old Presbyterian Church gave up infant damnation as a part of their creed. They took it out of their constitution and there was no longer any reason for staying out. Of course, we Presbyterians could do more good if we were united.

'That's the reason that most of us Cumberlands decided to unite. But a lot of the old hard-shells refused to come in.' The split had caused a lot of lawsuits as well as hard feeling. I remember many stories that the old man and his fellow preachers used to tell about church fights over property. In some cases the Cumberlands retained the property. In others, they lost and it went to the new united church.

'A lot of us Cumberlands who went over to the Presbyterian Church U.S.A. were called Yankees. I remember one of the old preachers used to call me a "nigger-lover" because I joined the Northern Church. "Well, Jim," he would say, "I hear you joined the nigger church. Well, Jim, I don't mind niggers but how do you stand to smell them? I just can't stand the smell of niggers. How do you like being in a nigger church, Jim?"'

'What did you say to him?'

The old man laughed. 'You may be sure I put the old fool in his place. I told him that the negro people were entitled to a place in the Kingdom of Heaven just as much as the whites. I asked him what he would do when he went to heaven and found Negroes there.'

'What did he say?'

'Well, he said it was all right with him if they didn't smell up heaven. And I venture to say that I gave him such a lesson in church democracy that he didn't ever forget. I told him there was a place for such snobs as he and that the Devil was pulling him straight down to hell and that he probably wouldn't have to associate with either poor negroes or poor whites. He could stay down in hell with the worldly rich and their sycophants and the rest of the hypocrites. After I gave it to him for about an hour, he left, and he never did bring up the negro question again.'

All the time the old man had been talking we were getting closer to Dwight. 'Maybe we should stop by Aunt Nancy's and dry our clothes,' the old man said. We were still pretty wet.

I guess we looked bedraggled when we drove up to Aunt Nancy Nine-Killer's. 'Why, Brother Mac,' she said in her shrill voice, 'git down and come in. We 'lowed not to see you today on account of the high water. Tom says nobody can't get across big Sally. Worst flood in forty years.'

We went into the house and Aunt Nancy built up a

fire in the big rock fireplace and we pulled off our shoes
and socks and dried our feet. Aunt Nancy sat down, filled
her corncob pipe with some home-grown tobacco, and
puffed slowly after she had lighted it with a taper.

Aunt Nancy had been born in Sequoyah County eighty
years before. She hadn't been on a train but once and out
of the county but twice in her whole lifetime.

Most of the furniture in her house was home-made.
The chairs were of hickory. On the wall of the big room
hung a long bow, a reminder of long gone days when game
in Oklahoma was plentiful and the Indians used the bow
and arrow. On the rafters above our heads hung quilting
frames and on the wall hung bunches of tobacco put there
to dry, long strings of red peppers and gourds cut in different shapes for dippers and bowls.

'Yes, Brother Mac, I remember worse floods than this
one,' said Aunt Nancy, as she puffed on her pipe. 'It was
in the days before the white man came to this country.
The Arkansas was two miles wide and all the bottoms
were full.'

'Well, Aunt Nancy, it's almost church time. We've
got to get started. I'm afraid we've missed Sunday
School,' said the old man.

'You and the boy go on and I'll be along as soon as
Mary hitches up the buggy pony,' said Aunt Nancy.

'Where's Hez?' the old man asked.

'Oh, that young buck,' said Aunt Nancy. 'Brother
Mac, that young buck won't work. Probably out drunk
somewhere. All he'll do is gamble, drink, and fox-hunt.
Reckon that pack of dogs of his eats more than me and
Mary and Faz.'

'Where's Mary and Faz?' asked the old man.

'Out milking. The bell cow lost her bell and they had to scour the woods to find the cows this morning.'

'Aren't those girls of yours ever going to get married?' asked the old man.

'Reckon they don't see no use of men. What with Turkey's boys all drunkards and no-goods. Brother Mac, whiskey has ruined the Indians. I can remember when they spoke with a straight tongue, when my people were respected and honored in all the land. They were feared, but now the Indian is laughed at as an old woman. He is cheated of his land as a child is cheated of a trinket. Time was, Brother Mac, when my nation was feared and respected.' Her old eyes flashed. 'I know because the old women told me when I was a girl. But that was before the white man took our land and gave us instead firewater and broken promises. With the war they took our slaves and burned our homes, drove our cattle away. Now they have got our land or most of it.'

We left the old woman standing on the porch of her old-fashioned house with the open hallway running through the center. The old man told her to hurry on to church, but she didn't hear him.

While he was preaching at Dwight this Sunday, some local toughs from Sallisaw came out to have some fun. They clanked in and out of the building talking in loud voices. The old man stopped in the middle of his sermon and looked at them without saying a word. The boys, at that instant, were sitting in the back seat of the church house laughing and talking.

When the old man stopped preaching everybody turned

and looked at the boys in the back of the room. They persisted in talking for a minute or so, but as the silence grew heavier they lowered their voices and finally stopped altogether.

Even then the old man did not resume his preaching. He just stood there and looked. His gray eyes were sharp as pinpoints.

Then he started speaking and his voice was so low that those in the back could scarcely hear. There was not a sound in the old church house except the measured voice of the old man that seemed to cut the atmosphere like a knife.

His voice was aimed at the little bunch of funsters on the back seat and it sounded like that of a judge pronouncing a death sentence.

'God will not be mocked. God will not permit this place of worship to be desecrated. This is a house of God, a temple of the Lord.' As he spoke, he raised his voice. Now he boomed out and his voice seemed to shake the walls. 'I, the servant of Jehovah, my God, will preserve order here and those who have no respect for themselves or for their families, their mothers and their God will leave. *Get out, get out!*' And his voice shook the rafters. 'Get out of the house of God. Do not profane the house of God by your presence. Verily, I will scourge thee from this house of worship as Jesus scourged the money-changers from the Temple.'

The boys on the back seat seemed completely awed. They twisted uneasily in their seats, not knowing whether to leave or not. Then another slight pause, but before the echo had died down the old man took a step forward, banged his big fist on the stand. This left no doubt in the boys' minds as to what they should do. They fairly ran from the room.

The old man stood and looked after them a few seconds; then calmly resumed his sermon. 'And the Lord said verily, "He that ruleth his spirit is greater than he that taketh a city."

'I have always said that gentleness and modesty and humbleness and kindness are the best traits that a man or woman can have. Jesus said, "Suffer little children to come unto me." And some people act like he meant that he wanted the children to get close to them and give them a hiding.

'No, God gives us rest and comfort and shelter when we are weary and heavy-burdened. When good Christian men and women are weary from carrying their great burdens, when the cross of life seems almost too great, then Jesus comes, the gentle compassionate Jesus, and presses a cup of cool water to the dry and parched lip — a cool cloth to the aching brow. He anoints my feet with oil. He brings me to the cool waters. He restoreth my soul.

'When we are trying to follow the way, when we are stumbling, when we are weary, when we are tired of fighting the Devil, the worldliness; when we feel that all is lost, then the Lord comes and gives us spiritual refreshment that we may continue the good fight.

'Oh, I remember, dear people, when I was a boy, how my mother would leave us children and go into the back room and closet herself with the Lord. She was weary, she was heavy-laden. She was tired of the fight. Her husband, my good father, was at war and she was trying to keep the wolf from the door. No wonder the way seemed dark and the burden heavy. No wonder she called on God to help her.

'And let me tell you, my friends, when my mother (who is now in Glory) came from that room after consultation with her Saviour, her eyes were shining and the spirit was strong in her. She taught those five fatherless children to pray, to go to church and to love the Lord. And she gave all those children the spirit. She instilled into them a love of the Lord.

'And although she, one of God's angels, couldn't continue her life in this world, for God needed her up there in Glory, the results of her work go on.

'Some of you people have lost loved ones. God has taken them to his bosom. God has needed them up there. And we should not feel sorrow at their passing, only happiness. For they are in Glory and we must suffer in this evil world.

'The world is filled with evil. Even now, this evil is at the door of this house of worship. Even now, on this day, in this house, in this hour, God was mocked.

'Despair not, O Christians. The faith you have in Jesus will carry you along from day to day, from hour to hour. It will help you to execute each task with fortitude and courage. Meet your God in private from day to day and in your place of worship in spirit and in truth.'. . .

After a few songs the old man prayed. 'O God, look down on us here gathered together to worship Thee. Look down, O God, on this little community and bless the souls that are congregated here. And especially bless, O Lord, those that have had some special sorrow, those that have lost loved ones, relations, and friends, and console them, O Lord, in their hour of distress. Let them be reminded that in heaven there is no more suffering and no more sickness and no more sin. For verily, thou hast prepared a house of many mansions; thou hast prepared this house for us. And at last when death brings us release from this worldly world, this place of trials, of crosses and of burdens, we will gather home. Home to the Father, the Son and to the Holy Ghost, thrice blest and consecrated and made eternal. Now may the spirit of God and the light of our Lord pervade our souls and may heaven bless us and keep us forever and ever. Amen.'

The people were attracted mightily by the discourses of the old man about the rewards of the Christian man or woman. Life was hard in that frontier community and most people were wicked, heedless of the promises of God, and many of the old folk felt that it would be a great relief when they were called to Glory.

When the old man spoke of these things, they responded with occasional amens and sighs and sometimes tears. Many is the time I've seen the old man draw water by such sermons.

After the service a lot of the people begged us to go home to dinner with them. Everybody asked everybody else to go home with him. 'Come, go home with me.' — 'No, you come.' — 'We killed the old red rooster.' — 'Might scare up a watermelon if the boys ain't et all of 'em.' — 'Better come go home with us.' — 'No, you folks come.'

We went home with a full-blooded Indian and his family. The man couldn't speak a word of English, but the old man had picked up some Cherokee and they could talk a little. They had a good dinner for the preacher, fried chicken and a lot of Indian dishes I never had tasted before. They were good though.

The Indian lived in a pretty good house for that county. It had three or four rooms and a big porch running around the front and through the center. We ate in the center hallway. It was a hot day and the flies were swarming. They had buttermilk, and a ring of flies lined the edge of the glass while great swarms of them buzzed around the table. Two little Indian girls stood on each side of the table with a big green brush and waved it to keep the flies away. Nobody in that country thought of screens any more than they thought of bathtubs or electric lights.

While we were eating a little brown papoose lay sleeping on a pallet near-by. Its mother occasionally took a brush and shooed the flies off the baby.

We didn't get home that day until about six o'clock. Although the sun was two hours high it was feeding time.

IT'S THE LEAKS

'WHAT I want to do,' said the old man, 'is to put this place on a paying basis. There's no reason why we can't sell enough stuff to support us.'

'I thought we had been doing pretty well,' said my mother. 'We raise all we can eat.'

'You forget that a lot of money is being spent here all the time. For instance, I've been paying Charley twenty-five or thirty dollars a month for a long time and I can't afford to keep it up. I tell you, wife, we've got to cut down on expenses.'

'You mean you are going to let Charley go?'

'Yes, I can't afford to keep him any longer.'

'But you've still got money in the bank. And surely you aren't going to take the boys out of school.'

'Yes, I've got money in the bank and I'm going to keep it there. I believe that the time to economize is when times are good. A good manager and a good provider always puts a little aside for a rainy day.

'Of course,' he added gruffly, 'your idea is to blow everything in. You probably want me to buy one of these gasoline buggies and get in the swim.'

My mother sighed and said nothing. To his dying day the old man insisted that she was extravagant and didn't know anything about business, although the Lord knows she spent precious little on herself and it was to a great extent the result of her hard work and good management that the farm was a success. To hear the old man talk you would think that he had done it all by himself and that she wanted to blow in everything on clothes and luxuries.

My mother had long ceased to argue with the old man on this point. She was the most patient, philosophical woman I ever saw.

The old man kept insisting that the farm was run in the most spendthrift manner. 'It's the leaks,' he would say repeatedly, 'it's the leaks. I am being ruined because of the leaks — more is going out than is coming in.'

What the leaks were none of us were able to determine, unless it was the old man's habit of constantly buying more land during all the time we lived on the farm.

Roy Frye, his lawyer, watched the tax lists, and when there was a good piece of land put up for sale he notified the old man. Frequently the old man would pick up good

land for a dollar or two an acre. Sometimes he didn't get
it because the owner bought it back in the time he was
allowed. But he had to pay the old man eighteen per cent
on the money he had put into it, and thus the old man
came out ahead anyway.

A lot of the land the old man picked up for a song was
timbered. This was important because our own wood
supply on the farm was beginning to run low.

One of our main problems was keeping up the fences.
Some of the posts rotted off in a few years at the top of
the ground and new ones had to be supplied. But the old
man always had a big supply of posts on hand, and he had
a way of treating them so they would not rot. First he
skinned all the bark off; then he dipped the lower end, the
part that was to go in the ground, into a creosote solution.

'That will preserve the wood,' he said, 'for ten years.'

Most of the posts we used were made of post-oak timber, but occasionally the old man got a chance to buy
locust timber, and he never passed it up, because a post
of this wood would last for twenty years.

The old man bought up timberland for fuel too. He
said that a man that would not keep a good supply on
hand was not any account, and we spent the rainy days in
the shed sawing and splitting wood with the bucksaw and
the axe.

'One of the ways I want to increase our money income,'
the old man said, 'is to raise more hogs. There is good
money in hogs now, what with pork going up on account
of the war.'

That year the old man expanded his pork-raising. He

bred four sows. 'That will give us twenty-five or thirty pigs for next year,' he said.

'But there won't be enough corn to feed all those pigs,' I said.

'You just wait and see,' replied the old man. 'This year I'm going to put the north field in corn for the first time. It's rich enough now to raise it.'

That field ought to have been rich. The old man had spent a lot of time and money on it. He had hauled hundreds of loads of rocks. And he had turned under a green manure crop annually for five years. The dirt was filled in behind the dams almost even with the land on either side. The succession of dams down the hill where the gully had once been looked like great stair steps.

'With that field and the richest part of the Cassidy ten in corn,' the old man said, 'and an extra field of goobers, we ought to have enough feed.'

'It seems to me,' said my mother, 'that you are going to need Charley worse than ever, because the extra fields of corn will take a lot of work.'

'Don't you worry about that, wife,' replied the old man. 'The boys and I will swing it. They are big enough to make full hands now. We will have to hump it, though.'

The time approached for Charley to leave, and we sure hated to see him go. He had become part of that farm. Even the old man showed regrets.

'Well, Charley,' he said, 'times are so hard, I guess I'll have to get along without you. You've been a good worker but the boys are big enough to plow and I am not able to keep you.'

'Oh, that's all right,' replied Charley. 'I was figuring

on making the harvest this year anyway. They say they're paying five dollars a day on account of the war. I can make a lot of money. But don't work the boys too hard.'

'All right, Charley, but you can stay on the rest of the week. I'll give you your money now.' And he wrote out a check.

On Saturday Charley packed his things and slipped out the back way while the family was eating supper. I was bringing the milk from the lot and saw him sneaking out.

'Why, Charley,' I said, 'aren't you going to tell us good-bye? You know my mother was expecting you for supper.'

''lowed I'd leave now. I'm in a hurry to get started for the harvest.'

'Well come on up, Charley,' I insisted, 'and tell the folks good-bye.'

'Listen, Bub,' said Charley. 'I ain't going to tell nobody good-bye. I don't believe in saying good-bye. You know, I will always like to feel like I'm still here and I want everybody to feel the same way. If I said good-bye I would feel like I was gone for good and you folks would feel like I was gone.' Charley kept talking slower and slower and finally looked like he was going to choke up.

'All right, Charley,' I said, 'if that's the way you want it. I know the folks will understand.'

'There's something I want you to know, Bub,' continued Charley. 'You know your old man works you boys and everybody around here awful hard. He's considered the hardest man to work for in the country. But there's something about him that gets you after a while. I can't explain it but it does, anyway, and I don't know why.' Charley stopped talking again, unable to go on. And in a minute he sputtered, 'Oh, hell, Bub, if I don't stop talking I'll be acting like an old woman.' And he turned abruptly and walked down the back road which led to the section line.

I stood and watched him go out of sight — his pack strapped on his back and his slight energetic figure moving rapidly down the road.

We never saw Charley again. He left for the harvest and was never heard of. Something must have happened to him, because I believe he would have come to see us if he had had the opportunity.

That year the corn crop was good. We filled the old crib to the top and the hay barns were filled also. The Cassidy ten was already giving good results. It had been two years now since the old man had bought the land, and already he was plowing over the upper end of the gully, which was deeper than a horse's back when he had bought it.

That year we had to stay out of school a good deal. The oat land had been broken in the fall but the old man insisted on breaking it again as soon as the ground thawed. Then he sowed the oats toward the last of February and plowed them in with double shovels followed by a section harrow.

School was out in May, and then we worked every day in the field. Some days we had three teams going, but most of the time we used single plows to cultivate the crops. There was the usual drouth, but it was short and the old man kept scratching the surface with shallow plows every few days.

That year I gave Nell the thumps while plowing the corn in silk and tassel. The high corn kept the air out and it was sure hot. That mare still had a lot of fire in her and I let her go. She walked fast up one row and down another, and one afternoon she began breathing so loud you could hear her a hundred yards away. The old man came down with some water to the field about three o'clock. When he heard the loud breathing, he got excited.

'Take that mare out!' he yelled. 'You've ruined her. She's got the thumps.'

We took Nell out and the old man put a blanket over her so she wouldn't catch cold.

'I knew we shouldn't have been feeding the work animals green stuff in this hot weather,' he said, 'but we'd run out of fodder. There's nothing like a bundle of fodder to keep a horse from getting the thumps in hot weather.'

Nell was always short-winded after that. We used to chase cattle with her bareback in the forty-acre pasture, and she always got winded after you had had her in a dead run for about half a mile.

Nell was the old man's favorite saddle-horse. She had a running walk that would carry him all day and she never got tired. All of us liked to ride a great deal, even my sister.

The old man said that no lady would ride astride and show her legs. When she and my mother argued that she could wear riding pants, he almost exploded.

'No decent woman wears pants,' he said. 'What is the world coming to?'

One day my sister bought a nice soft woman's saddle. We children all of us had bank accounts by this time and she bought it with her own money. The old man gave us what we made selling fruit, eggs, and vegetables. And why not? We worked hard enough to earn it.

My sister was just starting off on Nell when the old man saw her and exclaimed, 'What in the world are you doing on that man's saddle?'

Just then my mother came out. 'Now, listen, Mr. McDonald,' she said, 'there's no reason why this child shouldn't ride astride. She can't stay on that ridiculous sidesaddle any more. Suppose the horse ran away — she might get killed. You can't stay on the sidesaddle when the horse is running.'

The old man was vexed. 'Now,' he said, stomping his foot, 'Mrs. McDonald, you go into the house. And you,' he said, looking sternly at my sister, 'get down off that horse.'

'I'll do no such thing, Mr. McDonald,' my mother replied. 'And sister,' she said, turning to Beatrice, 'stay on that horse.'

The old man almost had apoplexy, but he knew that my mother was really aroused and that he could not bully her when she really set her head.

He stomped his feet and went into the house, slamming the door so hard the windows rattled. The sidesaddle was not mentioned again and my sister rode astride after that.

That winter something happened that interfered with the old man's plans for making money on the farm. The rats ate up a lot of the corn so that he had to buy some in the spring. Formerly we had kept the rats down with cats, but this year the old tabby died. The others disappeared one by one. I suppose some disease broke out among them. Gross Irwin said it was because they had been eating so many rats. They did eat a lot of rats. I've seen six or eight big rats lying in the toolhouse where Tabby kept her kittens. She'd kill them and bring them to the young cats. She was the best cat I ever saw.

We didn't discover the harm that the rats had done until late in the winter when we had used up the corn in the front of the crib. Toward the back we found little but cobs, shucks, rat nests, and excrement.

We took Colonel and Ring, the two dogs, and had a big killing. We took clubs and hit at the rats after they ran out of the corn. The dogs killed a lot of them and the old man killed one with his bare hands; not until it had bitten his finger, though. We must have killed fifty rats that day.

But the damage had already been done. The rats had destroyed at least half our supply of corn.

'I'll fix them,' said the old man. 'I'll build a rat-proof crib.' And he set about building the crib right away. He took tile, set the end with the lip in concrete, and then filled it with cement. On top of the upright tiles which were to serve as pillars for the rat crib he placed sheets of galvanized iron two feet square. Then he constructed his crib on these pillars, laying the joist across them. The crib was about three and a half feet, I guess, from the ground, and no rat ever got into it. The layer of sheet iron which extended out several inches all the way around kept them from jumping, and they couldn't climb up the tile.

'The farmers in this country lose a great deal of feed to the rats,' remarked the old man. 'But from now on, no rat is going to eat any corn of mine.'

The money gradually began to come in. The next fall we sold fifteen dressed shotes to the local butcher for ten cents a pound. We also sold two young Jersey heifers, that had just come fresh, for a hundred dollars apiece. We sold a lot of fruit, several hundred bushels of peaches for from one to three dollars a bushel, and lots of cream, milk, butter, and eggs. My mother now had a flock of a hundred and fifty hens.

I remember many's the time I used to go out and pick up from six to eight dozen eggs a day. We sold a lot of friers too. We had learned the market and tried to sell our stuff when it was the highest price. The year when the prices were best we cleared over two thousand dollars on our rock and air farm. The old man made a lot of money on his other farms too. Cotton was a good price and the money poured in.

Everybody went cotton crazy and planted bigger and bigger fields of it. There was a boom in cattle too. Cattle-buyers and speculators paid fabulous prices for blooded herds, and the banks furnished the money.

Money became easy. Everybody had plenty in those days. And everybody speculated in land, cotton, and cattle. But the old man still, of course, refused to plant any cotton on his home place. 'This boom won't last,' he said. 'Year in, year out, the farmer who raises his meat and his feed crops in a small way with a variety of crops will come out richer in the end.'

Of course everybody laughed at him. Even Uncle Green

disagreed. 'Jim,' he said, 'I never could have paid for my new home if it hadn't been for cotton.'

'Cotton, Green, will eventually ruin you,' the old man responded. 'Just as it has the other farmers. Oh, yes, you'll get high prices for a year or two, then the whole thing will collapse.'

But the old man was making money too. Nobody could deny that now. Uncle Henry on one of his visits admitted he had been wrong.

'Jim, you've turned this rock and air farm into a gold mine. You've built it up and you've made it pay. I've got to give you credit. I never thought you could make it. No, I never did. This farm was once a big joke; now it's generally conceded that it's the best-paying little farm in the country and that you are the best farmer.'

THE GOOD LORD INTENDED FOR THE
YOUNGER GENERATION TO USE ITS HEAD

ONE Sunday when I was riding with the old man to Dwight, he talked leisurely as we rode through the hill country. Ordinarily, he was too busy to talk much to his children. He went at a fast clip from early morning until late at night. He was busy with his crops, his dams, and his churches. He attended not only to his own business but ministered to the souls of the people in Sequoyah County.

'Son,' he said, 'there are two things that we all should strive for — Salvation first and solvency next.'

The neighbors to whom he had given this advice laughed behind his back sometimes. 'The old man McDonald says he wants salvation first and solvency next,' they would say, 'but he's really mostly interested in solvency. Somebody ought to tell him that when he's driving a hard bargain. He's looking out for salvation, all right, but he's so sharp he'd trade the last shirt off his neighbor's back.'

They never said anything like that to the old man's face. They were probably a little too hard on him. They were a little jealous because he had accumulated some property and lived in a big white house.

Even in the old man's sharp bargains, he followed out his theory of religion. 'The Lord watches out for those who watch out for themselves. I believe the Lord intended for me to accumulate property. If I didn't how could I carry on his work? If Henry didn't accumulate property how could he support the church? No, the Lord never intended for his people to bury their talents like the lazy fellow in the Bible did.'

The old man was getting rich in a small way. He had bought a lot of land when it was cheap, and now with high prices he had to pay a big income tax. But he always considered that he was a poor man.

'I belong to the common herd,' he said. 'I will never have so much money that I'll be ashamed of my old daddy, who was so poor he couldn't afford to build a privy. We always went to the woods when I was a boy.'

One of the old man's favorite jokes was about the time he went to Jackson, Mississippi, when he was a boy.

'I didn't know then that people had privies inside their houses and I looked all over town for some bushes. Finally

I asked somebody and he showed me a privy. I had never seen one before.'

'Yes,' he said, 'I want you boys to remember that you come from the common people, the poor people. No matter how high up you get in the world or how much money you make, don't forget your old daddy and his teaching. Work hard, spend little, and don't put on blue-bellied airs.'

But in spite of the old man's feeling about the poor, he came to be disliked because he was making money. He lived in a big white house and owned three farms, so that the brothers didn't like to contribute to his salary any more.

'Why should I give anything?' asked Brother So-and-So out at Badger. 'I don't have as much money as the preacher. I can't live in a painted house.'

There was also some feeling against the old man because of what he said about bank robbers. Sequoyah County has produced more outlaws than any place in the Southwest, and a lot of people were proud of it. I heard people say more than once, 'Henry Starr is no robber; he's better than the crooks in the banks. He's just getting back a little of the money that the bankers have stolen.'

Naturally the old man sided in with the bankers at Sallisaw and against those who spoke up for the outlaws, though he said that most bankers were crooked. 'The McDonald crowd is not responsible for the system. There never was a more honest boy than Henry.'

Some of our close neighbors were outlaws. There were four in one family who lived a mile from us. Two of them were killed robbing a bank and two others were sent to the pen.

At the time when I was in high school, Henry Starr was supposed to have reformed. He had reformed three or four times, was pardoned out of the pen and all, and had promised not to rob any more banks, but every year or two the urge to rob would come on him. They said it made him sad to see the bankers getting all the money from the poor. Finally Henry would get out his gun and sit on the porch and shoot the chickens' heads off. They said it was a sign he was getting restless again. He was a crack shot and could shoot a chicken's head off at twenty-five yards, shooting from the hip with a thirty-eight in a forty-five frame.

It was a sad time in Sallisaw when Henry got killed. He and his gang held up a bank at Harrison, Arkansas, and a banker stepped out and shot him in the side with a twelve-gauge. He died in a few hours. His gang started to fire on the banker but Henry stopped them, saving the life of the man who killed him.

Uncle Josh came by our house the day after this happened. 'Have you heered the news, Bub?' he asked me. He looked like he was about to blubber.

'Why no, Uncle Josh,' I said. 'What's the matter?'

'Henry Starr is dead,' he said. 'Poor Henry was killed yesterday.'

'Too bad,' I said.

'Heered it was a banker at Harrison City. Drawed on him from behind, I heered. Poor Henry!' moaned Uncle Josh, with the tears running down his cheeks. 'Poor Henry. And he was as good a man as ever throwed a gun on a banker.'

When I told the old man, we saddled up and hot-footed it to town. 'I want to talk to Henry,' he said.

'Come back to the private office, Jim,' said Uncle Henry. 'Did you hear the news? Did you hear about Henry Starr?'

'Why, yes, Henry,' said the old man, 'and a good thing too.'

'Not so loud. Wait until we get back in the office. Now, Jim,' said Uncle Henry, 'I want to caution you against talking too much about Henry Starr. You know practically everybody in the county was his friend.'

'Yes, but he was a grand rascal, a bank robber, and I'm going to speak out.'

'If you do it'll hurt you and it'll even hurt this bank. I'm glad. They ought to give that banker a medal. Somebody ought to have killed Henry Starr a long time ago, but don't say I said this. Insurance rates ought to go down now. You know, I never felt that this bank was safe while Henry Starr was alive, but don't repeat what I said,' said Uncle Henry.

'Well, Henry, you know I always have spoken up for the right, but I'll think it over.'

Everybody mourned over Henry Starr but the old man. His part-Indian congregation would have liked him better if he had had a few kind words to say for Henry. He made himself unpopular out at Badger and Dwight by telling some of the elders privately that he wasn't sorry that Henry Starr was dead. The talk went around and there was some feeling against him. Church attendance fell off. Uncle Josh said, 'I heered talk that the preacher was a-siding with the bankers.'

The same year that Henry Starr was killed my mother raised the question of my sister going away to college.

Beatrice had now almost finished high school, and my mother felt that a year away from home would do her good besides add to her learning.

The old man was especially strict with my sister because she was a girl. He was a little suspicious of girls because he believed they didn't have enough gumption to look out after themselves. The result was that he frequently embarrassed my sister and her beaus and often would not let her go out of the house at all.

'Well, wife,' he said in answer to my mother's suggestion, 'you know I have always wanted my children to go away to college. Now, when I went to college it only cost me four dollars a month for my board. Yes, I went to Cooper's Institute at Tupelo, and got through on very little money. But I guess Daughter couldn't do that,' he said a little sadly, thinking of the expense, no doubt. 'I don't know about it,' he finally said. 'We'll have to find some good church school.'

'I already have one in mind,' responded my mother. 'I think Maryville would be a good school for Daughter. And it's cheap too,' she added, saving the best argument for the last.

So it was decided that my sister should go away, and though the old man groaned when it came time to pay the bills, he was very happy when one of his old friends who was one of the college trustees wrote how well his daughter was doing. 'There never was a McDonald who wouldn't go to the head of the class,' he said proudly when he read this report.

At the end of the year, when my sister came back from college, he accorded her more respect and privileges than

he ever had before. 'Beatrice has grown up to be a real
lady,' he said.

But the next fall there was a little crisis in the family
about my sister's marriage. She had gone to Fayetteville,
Arkansas, to take a business course and had decided to get
married. When she came home with the young man on
Thanksgiving the old man went up in the air.

'This girl is only a child!' he roared.

'But Papa,' protested Beatrice, knowing his weakness
for good stock, 'the Bates family is one of the oldest in
Arkansas.'

'Well, well — the Bates family,' said the old man.
'What did you say your name was, young man?' he asked
the young man, who had stood through this a little embarrassed.

'Well, well, Bates, huh? You any relation to Uncle Billy
Bates?'

'He's my father,' said the young man, 'and he sent his
best regards.'

'Well, well, and how is Uncle Billy?' asked the old
man.

He was to some extent satisfied, but he insisted on
making a trip to Fayetteville to inquire about the character of the young man as well as to get more information
about his antecedents.

After that he told his friends about the match, always
throwing in the comment, 'Good stock, I say — as good
stock as you'll find in Washington County. The Bates
family is one of the oldest and most respected families in
Arkansas. It's not a bad match, if I do say it.'

He confessed to me one time that although Uncle Billy

Bates was a fine gentleman he never was a 'money-maker.' He never told this to his friends, though.

The old man asked some of the kin out for the wedding. He performed the ceremony himself. But halfway through the service he broke down and blubbered. We were surprised to see him in tears. Beatrice and my mother were sniffling a little too. My brother and I were disgusted at all of the bawling. 'Anybody would think this was a funeral,' my brother said.

Now that we were all well fixed we boys began to change our ideas about things. Ever since I could remember we had always been hard up. Every penny had to be counted, and even though the family was never in actual want we never felt that we could live easy.

But now it was different. There was money in the bank. There were fat cattle in our pastures and there was plenty of meat in our smokehouse. All the old signs of poverty about the place were long since gone, and we children dressed better and had more spending money.

Accordingly we felt that now since we had plenty, we could blow in money if we wanted to. Everybody else was making money hand over fist and spending it. The old man had a few thousand lying in the bank all the time. He invested some of it here and there, bought some cotton-seed-oil stock and one of Uncle Henry's farms for twelve thousand dollars, and still had money left over.

But he was just as economical as ever. Worse, it seemed to us, whose ideas were changing about how money should be spent.

But the old man never changed a bit. 'I wish I never

had to spend a cent,' he said. 'I wish I never had to buy a new suit. I wish this suit would last always. I would like to always go to town with more than enough stuff to sell than I have to buy.'

However, the old man was never stingy about improving his farm. He kept his fences up and built his renters good barns. But he disliked modern gadgets, as he called them. He bitterly hated automobiles, believing that they, together with living out of a paper sack, were responsible for much of the poverty of the country.

He even refused to improve our home place if it involved a departure from the old way of doing things. We wanted him to modernize the place. All these years we had been using coal-oil lamps and we had no modern plumbing system in the house. We suggested that he put in a Delco system, but he wouldn't hear of it.

'It seems to me,' he commented, 'that a little money has gone to your children's heads.'

'But you've got plenty of money now,' I said. 'I think it would be a fine thing if you'd put in electric lights and a water system. You could put in a pump in the well with a tank and we could have a modern bathroom.'

'Nonsense, boy,' said the old man. 'We don't need those modern gadgets. The good Lord never intended all these modern contraptions. The old privy is good enough for me. Of course, on these cold mornings the cold seat is a little bit of a shock to our setters, but that's not the true pioneer spirit. Have you children got so tender and rich that you can't stand a little cold? The good Lord never intended for our setters to be so well protected.'

The old man went on in that vein. The Lord invariably

was on his side of the argument. And he always stated his case with such finality and such conviction that it would seem like the rankest heresy to disagree.

I ventured to argue with him on this issue, though, even if I had to contend with both the Lord and the old man. 'No, we're not tender, but we don't see why people of our standing in the community shouldn't have a modern bathroom and electric lights.'

The old man turned and looked at me like he was seeing me for the first time. He hesitated a long time before he spoke.

'How old are you, boy?' he asked.

'Sixteen.'

'I thought so,' he said, as if he had just made a great discovery, and still looked at me as if he were seeing me for the first time. 'Well, I declare, you boys are growing up. I've been so busy that I hadn't noticed.'

I was taken aback by all this discussion. 'What's that got to do with a modern bathroom?'

'Well, now, I should have expected something like this. Now that you boys are getting in long pants,' he said, 'you're getting to have ideas of your own. You're wanting to improve things.'

I was at a loss to know if the old man considered this a crime or not. I assumed that he didn't, though he seemed amazed, as though he had made a great discovery and hadn't quite decided whether our having an idea was a sin or not.

He stood and looked at me until I grew embarrassed. Finally he said, 'This is a good thing. I want my boys to think for themselves. The Lord intended for you boys to think, and I am not one to interfere with the will of the Lord.'

I was still confused but I ventured a remark to find out what he was driving at. 'Then you mean we can have a modern bathroom?'

'I said no such thing. Of course not. Why, a modern water system would cost over a thousand dollars. We can't afford it. Times are too hard. I've already got an estimate, and if we put in a modern light and water system it would cost two thousand dollars.'

'I don't understand,' I said. 'You said you wanted us to think. Now you turn down any thoughts we have.'

'Of course, of course, my boy,' said the old man kindly. It was rare that he assumed such a parental air, especially when we had asked him for something we couldn't get. 'I want you to think up all the new things you can. That doesn't mean your ideas are practical, but it means you are beginning to use independently the brains the good Lord gave you. The good Lord intended for the younger generation to use its head. And the Lord, in his infinite wisdom, put me here to keep you from throwing your money to the birds. That's what you boys would do if I weren't here. I want you boys to use your initiative now that you are growing up, but of course there has to be only one pilot for every ship. And I will continue to be the one on this ship.'

So it was. The old man continued to run his farm and his business, asking advice from everybody and taking it from nobody, believing himself to be the greatest progressive that ever lived, and that he spent money liberally when he pinched every penny as if it were the last.

The richer he grew the tighter he became. Yet there were times when he made a great effort to loosen up. Now that we children were older, we frequently pointed out some of what we considered his great inconsistencies.

'You don't think as much of spending a thousand dollars for a renter's barn as you do of getting a cold drink,' I told him one time.

This remark stung him a little, I think, for after that when I went to town with him, he would invite me into Luton's drugstore for a limeade.

'Come in, son, and have a limeade.' And when I made a motion to take money from my pocket he would restrain me. 'Never mind, never mind. Your daddy is paying for this. It can never be said that your daddy was a stingy man.'

Nevertheless it was said, and during those last years a great deal more than ever, both because the old man was a man of property and because in certain respects he became closer than ever.

For one thing, he became more attached to old things. He insisted on wearing his old brogan shoes and his old ragged suit. He had a pair of ragged gloves that he wore in the wintertime, and although he had three or four pairs of fine leather gloves that the older children had given him, he steadfastly refused to put them on. When we asked him why he didn't, he said, 'I am saving them. You children, of course, want me to wear out everything at once.'

He became more opposed to innovations, even those that did not involve the spending of additional money. Worden and I were in the barber shop with him one time when the barber asked him, 'Do you want it cut the new feather-edge style, Reverend?'

'No, no,' boomed out the old man without any warning. 'Style, style, style. That's all I hear these days. Style has ruined the world.'

We boys grew to ignore these outbursts. We realized it would do no good to argue with the old man. If any of his statements like these were questioned, he would launch into a tirade and end up by calling on the Lord to testify in his favor. And with the Lord on his side, he was unanswerable.

18

FROM TWELVE O'CLOCK ON IS
THE LORD'S DAY

MY BROTHER and I rarely spent the night away from home, but occasionally in the wintertime we went over to Uncle Green's house to go possum-hunting with his boys. In those days there was plenty of game back in the hills and with a good dog you could catch six or eight possums.

Since the hunts lasted until one or two o'clock in the morning, we stayed the rest of the night at Uncle Green's. Occasionally we got a coon, but not often; coons were scarce and hard to catch. A coon skin was worth many times more than a possum skin, and the hunter in Sequoyah County who caught a coon was considered pretty lucky.

We went over to Uncle Green's one Saturday in January, planning to stay all night and go to church the next morning at Price's Chapel, where the old man was going to preach.

The old man was a little worried about our possum-hunting on Saturday night. 'Now, you boys must remember,' he said, 'that from twelve o'clock on is the Lord's Day and that you must come in at twelve. You must not desecrate the Sabbath by going possum-hunting on the Lord's Day.'

'All right,' we said. 'We'll quit hunting at twelve o'clock.'

After we had fed and had supper we rode over to Uncle Green's. Hershel, Uncle Green's youngest boy, met us at the gate. 'Get down and unsaddle,' he said, 'and I'll feed your horses.'

'We'll just turn the horses into the lot,' I said. 'We fed them before we left home. How's all the folks?'

'Oh, they're all right,' responded Hershel. 'Claude and Ewing are getting ready for the hunt and Mama and Papa are in the house. You better go in and get warm. We won't be ready to start for a while yet.'

We went into the house and warmed up before the big open fireplace. Uncle Green was sitting before the fire reading by the light of a coal-oil lamp. 'How's Jim?' he asked. 'Why didn't he come too?'

'Oh, he couldn't get away,' I said. 'He and my mother

had to do the chores in the morning. They'll be over for Sunday School and church tomorrow.'

'Have you boys heard the good news?' asked Claude, who was sitting by the fire cleaning his gun.

'No, Claude,' I said. 'What good news is that?'

'Roosevelt is dead,' said Claude, without cracking a smile.

'Oh, Claude!' said Aunt Jennie, who had come in from the kitchen, 'you shouldn't talk like that.'

'I never did see a Republican politician I liked,' said Claude. 'They are a bad bunch.'

'I have always voted for the best man,' said Uncle Green, 'but I make sure first he is a Democrat.' There was a laugh all around.

'Do you remember,' spoke up Ewing, Uncle Green's other boy, 'when Uncle Clayton sent around a bowl of corn bread and milk to John Pope when Wilson was elected?'

'No,' I said. 'I didn't hear about that.'

'Well, it seems John Pope, who was Uncle Clayton's partner in the store, had said that if Woodrow Wilson was elected over Hughes, times would be so hard that all we could have to eat would be corn bread and milk. You remember the first day it was announced that old Hughes was elected and John went around and crowed over the red-hot Democrats like Uncle Clayton.'

'Yes, I remember that incident well,' said Uncle Green, and he laughed and slapped his leg, which was a habit of the McDonald brothers when they were amused about something.

'Well, when the word finally came in that Wilson was

elected, some of the boys sent around a bowl of bread and milk to John. The result was that John was so put out about it that he wouldn't discuss politics for a long time.'

'How is Emma?' asked Aunt Jennie.

'Fine. She said she would see you tomorrow,' my brother answered. 'How have you been, Aunt Jennie?'

'Oh, I haven't been very well. I am pretty well worn out right now. There's been so much to do lately. I have to stay on my feet all the time.'

'I don't know why you're so tired all the time, Jennie,' said Uncle Green. 'Just a little cooking, cleaning, milking, and washing shouldn't wear you out. You've only got ten people to cook for and four cows to milk.'

'I guess Mama's just lazy,' said Hershel.

The conversation continued like this without anyone's cracking a smile. I suppose this was some of the McDonalds' dry wit. Everybody knew that Aunt Jennie was the hardest-working woman in the country. She set one of the best tables and her cellar was always full of fruit. We never went to her house that she didn't insist that we take home a jar of her best preserves, a pie, or some other delicacy.

'Well,' Claude said, 'if we're going to catch any possums we'd better be getting started.' So off we went, Claude taking the lead with the lantern and Ewing following behind carrying the sack and the axe. The dogs had disappeared after they were turned out.

We headed north into Brushy Mountain for about a mile before we heard the dogs. Claude stopped and listened. 'Sounds like old Sport's treed,' said Hershel, but Claude shook his head. 'On trail,' he said.

We continued to walk in the direction of the baying of the hounds. It came clearly to us through the cold clear night air. The dogs sounded eager, expectant, and impatient. They were telling us that they were on the trail of a possum and that the trail was getting hot.

Suddenly the baying stopped. 'Have they lost the trail?' I asked.

'No,' said Hershel. 'Probably old Sport is circling the tree to make sure.'

Sure enough the voices of the dogs came again. But this time the tone was different. Now the baying was longer and drawn out.

'Treed,' said Claude, and picked up the lantern.

We found the dogs at the foot of a big tree. Claude circled the tree, holding the lantern high. 'There he is,' he finally said.

We gathered around closely and looked where Claude was pointing. Then we saw two shining eyes peering at us.

'Well, I sure hate to chop this tree down,' said Claude. 'Ewing, how about going up and getting the possum?'

'All right,' said Ewing. 'I'll shake him out,' and he started to climb the tree. He told us afterward what happened. When he got up close the possum let go at him and got filth all over his hat. 'It's a good thing I was wearing it,' Ewing said. 'It would have gone into my hair.' But he just laughed when the possum pulled this trick. 'I know what's the matter with you,' he said, looking up at it. 'You're skeered.'

He shook the animal out of the tree. When the possum hit the ground he started to run, but the dogs jumped on him and sulled him. Claude grabbed him by the back of the neck and put him in the sack.

Altogether we caught eight possums that night. The dogs found two in one persimmon tree eating their midnight lunch. 'Well, this sack is getting heavy,' said Ewing. 'Hadn't we better go in?'

We were halfway home when we heard the dogs again. 'On trail,' said Hershel. We stopped and waited. Then came the long-drawn-out call. 'Treed.'

We started toward the dogs. 'Guess we can't pass up this one,' said Claude. 'Sounds like they're trailing again.'

We walked on. 'Treed,' said Ewing. 'I'd bet my best shote that Sport is treed.' Then the voice of the dogs changed again.

'Trailing,' said Claude. 'I think I know what is wrong. Boys, we may get a coon tonight. The coon is trying to fool the dogs by running up a tree and then down again. The dogs bark "Treed" until they pick up his trail again.'

For two or three hours we walked up and down those hills. That coon led the dogs a merry chase. But as they got wise to the tricks of the coon, they picked up his trail quicker. Finally Claude stopped to listen. There was no mistaking that loud, insistent, triumphant wailing of the dogs. 'They've got him this time, boys,' said Claude, and he broke into a run.

We found the coon perched in a blackjack tree overhanging a dry gulch. His shining eyes stared at us out of the darkness. 'I'll cut the tree down,' said Claude, and he started chopping.

As the tree leaned down toward the little canyon the dogs, who had never taken their eyes from the coon, ran down the almost perpendicular side to jump on their quarry when the tree fell. But the coon, sensing what was going to happen, did not wait for that. He jumped. It must have been forty feet to the rocks below, but it seemed to me in the pale moonlight that the coon hit the rocks running.

But the dogs had anticipated this. The coon had not run more than a few feet when they were on him. We scrambled down the cliff and gathered about the bunch of dogs and coon. Claude was there ahead of us with the lantern.

In the light we saw a large furry animal who seemed to be all teeth and claws. There were five dogs and two of them were on top of the coon, who was lying on his back fighting for his life. Then the coon saw an opening. He grabbed the head of one dog in his claws while he ripped him savagely with his long sharp teeth. The dog could not stand such punishment and ran yelping away. Then the coon got hold of the other dog and gave him the same treatment.

Old Sport, the lead dog, had been circling this fracas. Suddenly he dashed into the middle of the fight and caught the coon in his stomach. The coon let go of the dog he was holding and turned his attention to Sport. He gripped his head and with his sharp claws ripped Sport's ears. He clawed him, bit him, and chewed him up thoroughly, but the old dog did not for a second release his hold. He had his teeth buried and wouldn't let go.

All this time Claude had been circling the fighting coon. As the struggling dog and coon thrashed about, he saw his chance and struck the coon a blow with the axe which broke his back. The dying coon rolled over. Even then, old Sport hung on to his death grip. For a few seconds he refused to turn loose.

We put the coon in the sack and went home. 'Well, this has been quite a night,' said Claude. 'We had pretty good luck.'

When we got to the house it was about four-thirty and Uncle Green and Aunt Jennie were already up, although it was two hours before daylight. 'My goodness!' I said. 'Why do they get up so early on Sunday? It's not near day yet.'

'Oh, they always get up in the middle of the night,' said Hershel.

At Sunday School we saw the old man and my mother. 'Well, did you boys have a good time?' he asked.

'Yes,' we said, but we didn't tell him we hunted on Sunday.

Before the service, Aunt Jennie called the old man to one side. 'Brother Jim,' she said, 'I want to ask you a favor.'

'All right, Jennie.'

'I want to ask you to preach the sermon you preached in Arkansas once about the life of Christ. I want you to preach the children's sermon. Don't you remember, that's what you called it.'

'Why, yes, Jennie. I remember. I hadn't intended to preach that one today, but I will. I see there are a lot of children here, and I'll speak to them and forget about the old folks.'

'The old folks will enjoy it too,' said Aunt Jennie.

When the old man started to preach, he said, 'I am

going to talk to the children today. I am going to tell
them the most beautiful story in the world.

'Once there was a couple who had no children. The
wife was sterile and unable to conceive, but an angel appeared to her and told her that she would become big
with child and that this child would be the forerunner of
Jesus Christ. The woman's husband, Zacharias, also had
a vision, and he was told that from the time of the con-
ception of his wife until the time of the birth of the child
he would become dumb and unable to speak.

'And so it came to pass that the child was born and
Zacharias recovered his power of speech and christened
the child John, who was to be the forerunner of Jesus
Christ.

'In the same year but a little later the Christ Jesus was
born to Mary and Joseph in a manger in Bethlehem.

'"*Therefore the Lord himself shall give you a sign; behold,
a virgin shall conceive, and bear a son . . .*"

'When Jesus was thirty years old and after he was bap-
tized by John, and after John the Baptist had prepared
the way, he went out into the world and preached. After
a while he returned to his home town and the people said,
"This man is no prophet. This is only the son of Joseph
the carpenter. He is no great preacher and teacher."

'And Jesus said, "A prophet is not without honor save
only in his own country."

'Wherever Jesus went great crowds of people followed,
attracted by his words of wisdom and his personality.
Jesus knew that he would not be on this earth long, so he
selected twelve disciples to carry on his work. They were
plain men, poor people as were the great crowds that
flocked to see and hear him.

'The scribes and Pharisees soon heard of Jesus and condemned him as a false prophet. They didn't like him because he was exposing their corruption. They had control of the church and they had perverted it to their own evil ways. They even utilized the House of God for commercial practices. In one case they had converted the tabernacle into a market-place. This angered Jesus so much that he drove the money-changers from the house of worship with a whip.

'Everywhere he went he condemned the hypocrisy of the Pharisees. One time he condemned one of them who in his prayer thanked the Lord that he was better than other people.

'But the thing that Jesus attacked most was the love of money. One man that wished to be saved went to Jesus and asked what he must do. "What must I do to be saved?" he asked. And he told the Christ that he had obeyed all the commandments. "You must give all your riches to the poor," said Jesus. "You must give away everything you have got."

'And the young man went away saying nothing because he could not bear to part with his wealth. "Verily," said Jesus, "it is easier for a camel to go through the eye of a needle than it is for a rich man to enter the kingdom of heaven."

'In those days it was something new for a man of God to associate with the wicked. Jesus believed that the sinful people should be saved, and he loved the repentant sinners better than he did the old church members.

'But the scribes and Pharisees objected to this. They criticized him when he ate with the publicans and they condemned him because one time a woman of the town, a loose woman, came and washed his feet in oil and dried them with her hair. But he blessed her and forgave her sins.

'Jesus loved the plain people. Most of the people that Jesus healed were poor. He made the blind see, the lame walk, and he restored to life those from whom life had gone. And Jesus loved the children also.

'"*Then were there brought unto him little children, that he should put his hands on them and pray, and the disciples rebuked them.*

'"*But Jesus said, 'Suffer little children, and forbid them not, to come unto me; for of such is the kingdom of heaven.'*

'"*At the same time came the disciples unto Jesus, saying, 'Who is the greatest in the kingdom of heaven?'*

'"*And Jesus called a little child unto him, and set him in the midst of them, and said, 'Verily, I say unto you, except ye be converted and become as little children ye shall not enter into the kingdom of heaven.*

'"'*Whosoever therefore shall humble himself as this little child, the same is the greatest in the kingdom of heaven.'*"

'Time passed and the time approached for Jesus to die. He had to give his life to save the world.

'Though Jesus was divine, he suffered more than any human being. He was subject to all the frailties of mankind. He was tempted by the Devil. He was taken to the top of a high mountain and offered the whole world if he would forego his trial.

'But he stood fast and said, "Satan, get thee behind me."

'Jesus was just as resolute when the time came for him to go to Jerusalem. He knew that if he went there the scribes and Pharisees would contrive to bring about his death. They were plotting to bring about his death because he was turning the people against the corrupt church system. They were afraid the people would turn them out if Jesus continued to expose them.

'But Jesus went down to the great city of Jerusalem, and on the way the people who loved him dearly gathered in great crowds and spread flowers along the way. Jesus was more thoughtful and pensive and sad than ever. He dreaded the fast approaching day when he must endure great agony.

'Finally Jesus arrived in the city at the time of the Passover feast, and the scribes and Pharisees consulted among themselves as to how they could bring about the death of Christ without arousing the anger of the people.

'Just before the day that Jesus was to undergo his great ordeal he called his disciples together for one last supper and as he broke the bread, he said, "Eat of this for it represents my body," and as he drank the wine, he said, "Drink of this for it represents my blood."

'And the twelve disciples ate. During this meal Jesus told his disciples that one of them would betray him and that another would deny him. Jesus said that the one who would betray him was at the moment eating from the same plate. And the disciples looked and saw it was Judas Iscariot. Judas had been paid thirty pieces of silver to betray the Lord. And Jesus told Peter that he would be the one to deny him. But Peter protested and said, "No, Lord, I would never do that. I would never deny you." And Jesus said, "Before the cock crows twice you will deny me thrice."

'After the last supper Jesus went away for a while for

one last conference with God. He was in mental and spiritual anguish because he knew that horrible suffering was soon to come. And he was in such a state of anguish that great beads of perspiration appeared upon his body that were as drops of blood.

'Saying, *"Father if thou be willing, remove this cup from me; nevertheless not my will, but thine, be done."*

'After Jesus had prayed he returned to the spot where he had left his disciples to watch and he found them asleep. He awakened them and asked them to watch again. Three times in all Christ returned and found his disciples asleep. And at last he said, resigned to their negligence, "The time is past; the hour is come."

'And he went into the city to face the scribes and Pharisees. On the way a crowd of enemies approached, and Judas Iscariot, who had received the thirty pieces of silver to betray Jesus, approached and kissed him, indicating to the men of evil that this was their man.

'So they took Jesus away. And a girl approached Peter and said, "You were with this man. You are one of his confederates. You are also from Galilee." And Peter denied this. Again Peter was accused of being a friend of Jesus, and again he denied it and he heard the cock crow. And again Peter was accused of being a friend of the Lord, and for the third time he denied it. Then the cock crowed for the second time and Peter, remembering the prophecy of Jesus, went away and wept bitterly.

'The Pharisees declared Christ guilty of blasphemy and brought him before Pilate, in whom was vested the Roman authority. At this time Rome ruled Palestine and the Jews had to get his consent to take the life of the Lord.

'Pilate questioned Jesus and marveled at his angelic and noble bearing. He knew that Jesus was innocent and he did not know what to do. At first he refused to condemn him. "I have examined this man," he told them, "and I can find no wrong in him."

'Now the scribes and Pharisees had assembled a crowd of their flunkeys and lackeys in front of the palace of Pilate, and they cried out for the blood of Christ: "Crucify him," they cried, "crucify him!"'

'And Pilate, intimidated by these outcries, turned and washed his hands in a basin and said, "Take him. His blood be on your hands."

'So Jesus was lead away clad in a scarlet cloak and the crowd spit on him and taunted him. A crown of thorns was placed upon his head and the long march began on the way to Calvary where Jesus was to be crucified, and the scribes and Pharisees were at last happy.

'On the long way to Calvary Jesus was subjected to all manner of indignities. He was spit on and pummeled and called in derision the King of the Jews.

'A few of the followers of Jesus were in that crowd. And one of them was so enraged at the ill treatment the Christ was receiving that he cut off the ear of the tormentors with his sword.

'Then Jesus touched the wound and made it whole again and rebuked his follower.

'When Jesus arrived at Calvary he was nailed alive to a great cross. The spikes were driven through his hands and his feet. And a sponge of vinegar was pressed to his tongue. The cross was then erected and a great sign was hung over it in Latin, Greek, and Hebrew so that all the multitude might read: "This is Jesus, the King of the Jews."

'On either side of Jesus to degrade him further were crucified two common thieves. One of the thieves jeered at Jesus with the crowd. And the people jeered at Jesus, saying, "If you are King of the Jews, why don't you save yourself? Where is the Temple you were going to rebuild? Come down from the cross if you are King."

'Through all this Jesus never said a word. He was suffering the most horrible pain but no word of complaint crossed his lips.

'"*He was oppressed and he was afflicted, yet he opened not his mouth; he is brought as a lamb to the slaughter, and as a sheep before her shearers is dumb, so he openeth not his mouth.*"

'Only once when the jeers of the crowd were the greatest, he looked up to heaven and cried out, "Father, forgive them. They know not what they do."

'And one of the thieves on the cross seeing the nobility of Jesus said, "Verily, you are the Son of God."

'Then Jesus turned his head and replied, "This day you shall dwell in Paradise."

'From the third hour to the sixth hour Jesus hung upon the cross. Then in the sixth hour the sky became overcast, the sun hid its face and thunder was heard and lightning flashed across the sky. Then some of those who had mocked the Christ became afraid.

'In the ninth hour Jesus turned his eyes to heaven and cried, "My God, my God, why hast thou forsaken me?" And then he died.

'And the sky was rent in twain and the world became dark and the earth trembled mightily and great fissures appeared on the ground. Then panic broke out among the

multitude and they ran away. They were smitten with ter-
ror. They realized now they had put to death the Son of
God, but it was too late. One of the centurions said,
"Surely this man was the Christ."

'Then came a man named Joseph, a good man, and got
permission to take the body of the Lord from the cross and
he caused it to be put in a tomb and sealed with a great
stone.

'And the scribes and Pharisees, remembering the prophecy of the resurrection, caused a guard of soldiers to be
put around the tomb of Jesus so his disciples would not
come and steal away the body of the Lord, claiming that he
had risen from the dead.

'And on the morning of the third day, Mary Magdalene
and the other Mary went to the tomb of Jesus and were
confronted by an angel covered by a great light. "Be not
afraid," said the angel. "The Lord is risen." And Mary
Magdalene and the other Mary went and found Jesus, and
he showed them the marks on his hands and feet where the
nails had been driven when he was crucified.

'Then Jesus assembled his disciples and told them to go
out into all the world and preach the gospel to all men that
they might be saved.

'Then Jesus who had died that all men might live again,
ascended to the house of his Father.'

Then the old man said, 'Children, let us pray together,'
and he bowed his head, and he and the children with one
voice prayed: 'Our Father which art in heaven, hallowed
be thy name. Thy kingdom come. Thy will be done in
earth, as it is in heaven . . .'

19

I'VE NEVER BEEN BEATEN

To BEGIN with, our farm was one of the poorest and hilliest in the country and the farmers laughed at the old man. They laughed at him because he was a preacher and he was telling them how to farm. But now they had to admit that his crops were better than theirs.

Our place was perfectly improved in every way. 'Everything is in apple-pie order,' said the old man. 'Barns, fences, and house in A-number-one shape. The house is easily worth four thousand dollars. You couldn't build it for less than four thousand dollars, or anyway thirty-six hundred dollars.'

It had cost about sixteen hundred dollars, I think, when he built it in 1912. But of course lumber and wages were much cheaper then. And in Sequoyah County everybody gave the preacher good prices. The merchants in town sold us everything at cost, and frequently in haying or hog-killing time the neighbors would come in and help out and wouldn't take a cent for it. When we boys went to the stores in town, though, to make a purchase, the merchant would charge us the regular price and the old man would say, 'Why didn't you tell him your daddy was a preacher?' He tried to get a reduction on everything.

One time when he and I went over to Fort Smith to see Uncle Doc Covey, the old man misplaced his cravat. He went into a store to buy one and the man said, 'That'll be twenty-five cents,' and the old man asked, 'Is that the regular price? I've always got my cravats at twenty cents, at cost.'

And the clerk said, 'Why?'

The old man replied, 'The preacher should get every-thing at cost. You oughtn't to charge me more than twenty cents for this cravat.'

The clerk and the old man had quite an argument. Finally the manager of the store was called in, and it seems he was a member of Uncle Doc's and Aunt Alice's church, so he let the old man have the cravat for twenty cents.

The preacher story was quite a joke in our family for years. 'Why didn't you tell the man Papa was a preacher?' my sister would say, whenever I bought anything.

The old man used to talk about the cotton system to Wayne Bonham, who was the largest landowner in the country. He and his boys managed thousands of acres. On part of their land they furnished sharecroppers, and the rest they farmed themselves by hiring hands.

'The cotton system, Wayne, has impoverished the South. You big landowners could discourage it, but you don't — you encourage it.'

'We can't help ourselves,' said Mr. Bonham. 'You know the banks won't furnish renters and sharecroppers unless they raise cotton. They say they can't collect rent. There is no way to check up on a corn crop. The farmer could steal half of it, but he can't steal the cotton because he has to register it at the gin before he can sell it.'

'The bankers judge everybody else as they do themselves, I suppose,' mused the old man. 'You know, Wayne, we are in the throes of a vicious financial system. The commercial class is gradually ruining the farmers and the land. Something has got to be done. I've tried to get my neighbors and renters to raise feed but they won't do it. They are slaves to King Cotton. If they would raise feed and grass instead they would eventually become prosperous.'

The old man had a farm back in the hills that he had picked up for a song. One day he and my mother were out driving and he stopped about a half-mile from the house on this farm. 'This is my land too,' he said.

'Mr. McDonald, don't you think you've bought enough land?' asked my mother. 'You have got a mania for it.'

Our hill place became known as a model farm. A man came down from Oklahoma City for the *Farmer-Stockman*, and after going over the place with the old man, he wrote an article extolling him and his ideas.

In many ways we had a good life on the farm. There

was plenty of everything. Our barns were overflowing, our crops were the finest, our cattle were fat, and our horses were the best-trained. It was a well-ordered little universe. Everything and everybody worked for six days because the Bible said, 'Six days shalt thou labor and do all thy work; but the seventh is a Sabbath unto Jehovah, thy God; in it thou shalt not do any work.'

One spring the old man was plowing in the three-acre field. That was as good land as we had. He stopped plowing, tied the lines to the plow handle, dropped a trace chain, and went into the house. My mother was cooking dinner.

'Wife, come down to the field. I want to show you something.'

'I am very busy,' said my mother.

'Oh, come on. I want to show you something.'

When they got down to the field the old man started the team. He had pulled off his shoes and socks and was walking along in the moist loamy dirt in the furrow behind the turning plow.

'Look at that, wife, look at that. Look at that rich dirt turning over. Isn't that fine? Look at the rich brown dirt that I'm turning. I tell you this is the only life.'

My mother turned without a word and went back into the house. 'Your mother,' said the old man, turning to me, 'is a city woman.'

The fall of the year was the time that the old man liked best. That was the time when his barns were filled, when his smokehouse was full of meat, and when the stock was the fattest. When we had company, our table was overflowing. 'Everything on this table,' the old man would say, 'was raised on the farm except the sugar and coffee.'

After dinner he would take the visitors out and show them his rat-proof crib. 'Look at that corn,' he would say. 'I raised that on my rock and air farm.

'Now I want to show you my cows. There's old Butter-cup. She gives six gallons of rich milk every day, and there are three of her calves and they are as fine heifers as you ever saw. I have been offered one hundred dollars apiece for them, but the boys don't want to sell. I give all the increase of the cows to the boys.

'Now let's go look at the potato house. Those walls are two feet thick. They are filled with sawdust. I raise one hundred bushels of sweet potatoes every year. This is my two-acre garden. We raise everything to eat that will grow. Originally it was very poor land, but I've manured it and built it up. No manure goes to waste on this place. Some of the neighbors say I run around after my stock with a shovel.

'Now here are my hay barns. I have got a system of curing hay after it is in the barn. Over there is the smoke-house. We killed sixteen hundred pounds of meat this year. When I came here I had one little scrubby sow, but I've built up the stock until my pigs are as good as any in the country. My shotes weigh two hundred pounds in six or eight months and I only feed them two or three weeks on corn. I raise small plots of peas, peanuts, and artichokes, and as soon as they've cleaned out one patch I turn them in on another. They root in the Bermuda too. The roots are good for hogs and the rooting helps the grass.

'Now come down into the cellar and I'll show you our canned fruit. We've got every kind of fruit put up that grows. I raise the finest peaches in the country on my rock and air farm. This place feeds my family and we sell enough produce to buy the boys clothes and give them bank accounts. They've got money in the bank; they have their own horses to ride, and my youngest boy has ten head of cattle of his own. And best of all, my boys have been taught to work and keep out of mischief.'

During all the years we had lived on our rock and air farm the old man had worked without sparing himself. One day my mother said to me: 'I do wish your father would stop buying land and working so hard. At his age he should take things easy.'

I laughed. The old man would work until he fell dead. I have never seen a man so full of energy. Ever since I had known him he had gone at top speed. Two thirds of the night he couldn't sleep; he had developed insomnia in his college days. Some of his friends said he traded his bed for a lantern when he went to college. At twenty-five he had a nervous breakdown; the doctors had given him dope without his knowledge and after two months he found out the truth. They had made a dope fiend out of him. He was in a frenzy and declared he would take no more dope. He walked all night long, night after night, and would come stumbling home at daylight, his eyes wild, his clothes torn. The doctor said he would lose his mind if he wasn't given some morphine. They tried to give him a shot but he fought like a wildcat. Four men could not hold him. He broke from their grasp, running from the house, crying, 'I won't be beaten. I'll fight to the end.'

I remember one time the old man took me out and

walked me over some new land he had bought for taxes. As we went along I thought of that early fight he had made and wondered how he would face his last battle. I could not believe he would acquiesce to defeat in anything. 'The peach orchard will be here,' the old man said, and he went on explaining his plans, telling me what a fine stock farm he was going to have. 'It is an ideal location. Plenty of water the year around; the hogs will get fat on the mast in the fall. There's grass for the cattle that can be supplemented by feed in the winter. Brushy Mountain will knock off the cold winter winds.'

We walked for two hours, climbing up and down the mountains and valleys, while the old man showed me where the land was and told me his plans. 'Let's sit down and rest.' We sat down. 'I am not as good a man as I used to be.'

Going back home in the buggy I looked at him. Something was wrong. The old man was tired. It was unbelievable. He had never been tired in my memory. Suddenly he seemed shrunken and bony like an old horse who has lost his teeth. I glanced down at his legs. They looked long and knotty like those of a newborn colt. He had changed imperceptibly in the last year and nobody had noticed. The truth dawned on me at last. The old man was getting old. Death of course, I thought, will come in a few years, and I shuddered when I thought of the interim. I felt that the old man would never accept old age.

He had always seemed old to me, not in the sense of decrepitude but in the sense of permanence. He was one of those unchangeable things in our lives which, like the hills and the sky and the land, would always be there. I had no great conscious affection for him. He had been too busy to treat me as a son except on rare occasions; yet I could not imagine life without him, because he dominated me and every living thing with which he came in contact. Without him none of us would have direction. In a sense there would be no purpose in our lives. There would be no use in living.

All this I felt as I sat in the old buggy, pushed almost out of the seat by the old man's spraddling legs. At least his magnificent barrel chest hadn't withered and his massive head with its high forehead would always be the same.

In the months that followed I watched the old man and his last fight. Old age was catching up with him, but his spirit remained young. He worked as he always had. He was here, there, everywhere, directing the hands, building his dams and fences, issuing orders, storming about more impatient than ever.

In the last few years his hearing had failed. We had to shout when we spoke to him and he yelled at us in return.

'Why don't you speak so I can understand you? Open your mouth when you speak to me. I'm an old man. I'm deaf — you know I'm deaf.'

It was plain that his strength was not what it used to be. It was amazing how fast he went down after the first sign of decay. Some men grow old slowly, ripen to a complacent old age, basking in an imaginary past, enjoying their dotage, like an old toothless hound who dozes by the fire on winter evenings and dreams of the hunt. But others, like the old man, who have always lived in the future, rebel and rage like an old stud who is no longer fit for service.

Thus it was with the old man. He would not rest. His family and his doctor pleaded with him to give up his preaching and his farming and to retire. 'I will die in the harness,' he said. 'I will not shrivel up like an old horse. I will continue to work.'

The end came fast. Fuming at the doctors who couldn't cure him of his weakness, impatient with his family, working when he could scarcely stand, raging against the inevitable that he wouldn't accept, the old man was difficult to live with in those last few months. He worried about his financial affairs, about his crops and his dams.

But in the long winter evenings the year before he died, occasionally we would have a long talk as in the old days. 'I have always considered that if Blücher hadn't arrived when he did, Wellington wouldn't have had a chance. For strategy, Napoleon has never had an equal. Napoleon would have been beaten later, though. The English were the rising power. Nobody could beat them.'

That last year the old man was forced to take to his bed part of the time. But every day he spent some time in the garden, walked down into the fields, looked at his green fields, pulled off his shoes and walked barefoot in the most freshly plowed ground. When we tried to help him to the house he flung us aside impatiently, roughly.

I think toward the last he came to realize the truth. When they came to take him to the hospital he did not create a fuss. We were afraid he would refuse to go, but he was in such a state of pain and weakness that he seemed another person. For the first time he took orders and obeyed the doctors and the family. We cried to see him so.

But when he was tucked into Cousin Jim's car, the old gleam came back into his eyes. He straightened up. 'These cars are bankrupting the country. Look at these farmers' places. Half the window lights out, the fences down, and not a cow or a chicken in the place, but a car sitting in the yard.' He fell back on the seat. 'I'm an old man. I am done.' And a moment later: 'I've never been beaten, never been beaten.' And he fell back on the seat again, relapsing into semi-consciousness.

As we approached the Arkansas River bridge he said, 'I want to be buried in a pine box as my mother was. We made it with our own hands.' When no one answered he said, 'Well, why don't you answer? Are my wishes to be ignored?'

'You must rest now,' said my mother, 'so you will be well again.'

At the hospital he grew rapidly worse. In his delirium he built dams again. 'That will stop the wash. Why don't you set out Bermuda? Now let a gully-washer come.'

He died in a few days in his sleep. The nurse who held his hand said that his pulse beat strongly up to the last. His final wish was not granted. He was buried in an expensive casket. His oldest son, Foster, bought a steel box to put it in to keep the water out.

The funeral services were held in the old church in Fort Smith where he had once been the pastor. The minister told what a good man he was and how many souls he had saved. He didn't mention the soil he had saved.

THE END

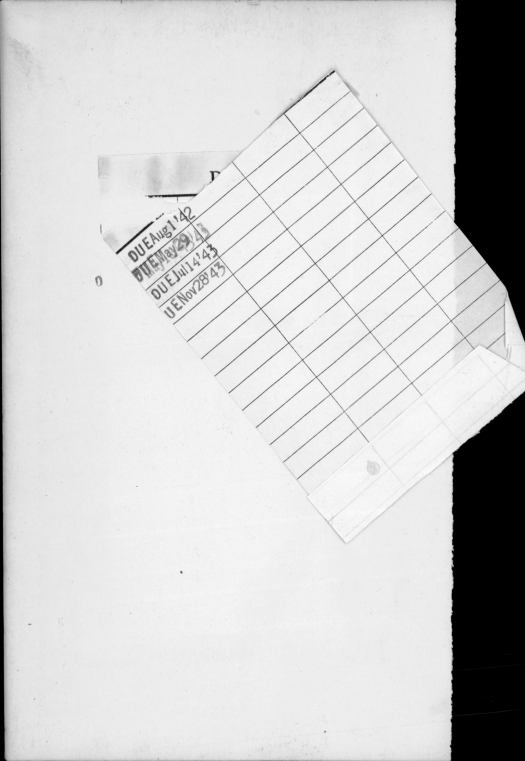